Sexplosion

A BIBLICALLY-BASED SEXUAL INTIMACY WORKBOOK FOR WIVES

by
Ramona N. Bailey

Contents

PART II: SERVING

PART III: KNOWING

APPENDICES

LIST OF ILLUSTRATIONS

Foreword

No subject creates more conversation, controversy, and confusion than the subject of sex. We are consumed by it and immersed in it. We can hardly escape its smothering influences. Our entire culture revolves around it. Sex sells magazines, movies, and TV sitcoms. It creates our images, determines our values, and defines much of our entertainment. The problem is, however, that the subject of sex has been removed from its original intent. Rather than being the unique, holy act of commitment it was created to be, it has been devalued into little more than an animalistic act bearing little or no resemblance to what God had in mind when He created this act of love.

When God created the first couple in Genesis, He gave them, as part of their marriage relationship, the awesome and unique capacity to thoroughly enjoy one another with no shame or hesitation. This marvelous act of pleasure was meant by the Creator for married couples to fully express their love, commitment, and enjoyment of one another without either the restraint of the pseudo moralist who acts as though sex is merely for procreation, or the unrestraint of the hedonist who has turned sex into an immoral free-for-all resulting in decadence, disease, and disgrace.

It is time for Christians to speak forthrightly about the subject of sex from a biblical perspective that also addresses the pragmatic real-life meaning of God's statement that the marriage bed is undefiled. Couples who love God and believe His Word should also know how to enjoy one another as God intended.

In this intriguing book, Ramona Bailey invites married couples to fully explore and experience God's special gift of sex. She clearly demonstrates that it is possible to be both spiritual and sensual within the context of a divinely ordained relationship. This book will help couples get over the shame, embarrassment, and ignorance of the subject of sex and begin to fully experience all God had in mind when He created such a powerful expression of love.

To be sure, this book may make you snicker a bit. It may even embarrass you at certain points, but when seen in the context of God's plan, which is clearly spelled out in this book, you will discover a new level of intimacy you and your marriage partner have never known before.

Anthony T. Evans
(Th.M., Th.D, Dallas Theological Seminary)
Senior Pastor of Oak Cliff Bible Fellowship, Dallas, Texas
Founder and President of The Urban Alternative

Acknowledgments

I thank my Heavenly Father for the glorious blessing of marriage in which we can experience the blessing of sexual intimacy.

A special and sincere thanks to my wonderful and dynamic husband, Joe. God has blessed me with a godly husband who fears Him and is committed to abide in the Word. Sweetheart thanks for faithfully abiding in the Word, washing me in the Word, *knowing* me in an understanding way, and loving me as Christ loved the church. Thanks for the *sexciting* sixteen years of *sexperimenting* to prepare this Workbook. I shout *hallelujah* for the *sexplosions* we have shared throughout our marriage.

Thanks to Sharon E. Greggs, M.D., a leading expert in the diagnosis and treatment of women's health issues, for your medical review. Armintia (Minti) Alcorn, I am very grateful to you for copyediting the first draft. You helped me to realize the first draft needed a major overhaul. Thank you for sharing your wisdom and for exhorting me to pursue ventures I would not have considered.

Thank you, Tina Strawn and Lisa Gardner, for critiquing and copy-editing. Sonya Reynolds, thanks for your support and prayers. Sonya, your wisdom, accountability, and encouragement kept me pressing forward.

Thank you, Bryan T. Bailey, for your artwork. God has truly blessed you with this talent. You are indeed appreciated. Thanks for freely giving of your talent.

The G-Spot illustration is taken from page 119 of *Dr. Ruth's Encyclopedia of Sex,* Copyright © 1994 by G.G. The Jerusalem Publishing House Ltd. Reprinted by permission of the Continuum International Publishing Group.

About This Workbook

This *Sexplosion* Workbook is written by a wife to address the specific sexual concerns of wives. It is comprehensive and overflowing with Scriptures, techniques, and illustrations. *Sexplosion* boldly addresses and explores what many Christians have erroneously considered to be "taboo," "off-limits," or "offensive." You are encouraged to pray against being embarrassed or ashamed by the direct and frank biblical teaching presented in this Workbook. It is not the intent to offend you but to exhort you to be bold and free in this wonderful gift from God—sexual intimacy!

This Workbook and others in the Sexplosion In Marriage Series™ is a beginning for the Christian community to begin to be bold and not intimidated to share God's freedom in the marriage bed. The Christian need not go to any non-biblical resource—whether television, video, magazines, or books—to seek knowledge on sexual intimacy. It is only through abiding in the Word of God that you can know the truth about sexual intimacy and be free in Christ to *sexplode*. If you do not apply God's Word, you will never *sexperience sexhilarating sexplosions*.

There are three biblical principles of *sexplosion*. These principles are in three parts:

Part I: **A**biding   Abiding in the Word of God.
Part II: **S**erving   Serving resulting in being served.
Part III: **K**nowing   Knowing "how to" *sexperience* a *sexplosion*.

If you abide in the Word, you can **ASK** and receive the full joy of *sexplosions* in your marriage. As you apply the biblical *sexplosion* principles in your life, the truth of God's Word will set you free to truly enjoy every aspect of sexual pleasure between you and your husband.

The authors have checked with sources believed to be reliable in their efforts to provide information that is complete and generally in accord with the standards accepted at the time of publication. However, in view of the possibility of human error or changes in medical sciences, neither the authors, medical experts, nor any other party who has been involved in the preparation or publication of this work warrants that the information is in every respect accurate or complete. They are not responsible for any errors or omissions or for the results obtained or alleged to be caused from the use of such information. Readers are encouraged to confirm the information contained herein with other sources. The *Sexplosion* Workbook is advisory only and is not to serve as a medical textbook or a substitute for the advice of your physician, who can discuss your individual needs, symptoms, and treatment.

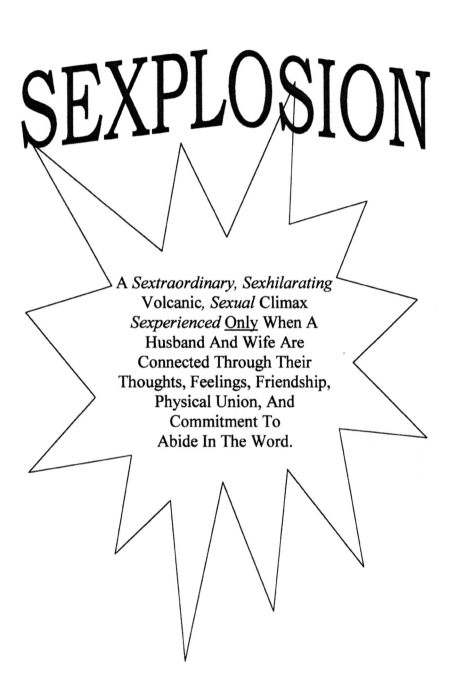

SEXPLOSION

A *Sextraordinary, Sexhilarating*
Volcanic, *Sexual* Climax
Sexperienced <u>Only</u> When A
Husband And Wife Are
Connected Through Their
Thoughts, Feelings, Friendship,
Physical Union, And
Commitment To
Abide In The Word.

How to Use This Workbook

This is not just a book; it is a "*Work*book." A Workbook means you must "work." In this Workbook you are encouraged to:

- ♥ Work through Scriptures to bring you to a more intimate relationship with God and your husband.
- ♥ Work through your own personal challenges, so you may experience victory over all that hinders you from freely enjoying sexual intimacy.
- ♥ Work on practical *sexercises* and assignments to apply these biblical *sexplosion* principles.

To experience *sexplosion* in marriage, the biblical principles and Scriptures must be read, studied, memorized, and applied. This

Workbook is not designed to be used in part, but in its entirety, from beginning to end. The various working components throughout the Workbook are:

❦ **Abide in the Word**. Throughout the Workbook you will be exhorted to read, study, memorize, and obey God's Word. The open Bible book symbol and the phrase *"Abide in the Word"* will list key Scriptures as they relate to the specific area being addressed. These key Scriptures can be life changing for you if you make the wise choice to abide in the Word.

❦ **Action Plan.** This Workbook requires you to take direct action to make changes in your life. This is not a Workbook for you to read for pleasure, but for you to be a doer and not just a reader or talker. Guidelines for developing and implementing Action Plans are listed in Appendix A.

❦ **Accountability/Spiritual Support Partners (ASSP).** A practical method to aid you as you implement your Action Plans and to encourage you to walk as Jesus walked. ASSP Guidelines are listed in Appendix B.

❦ **Assignments.** There are many assignments and *sexercises* for you to enhance your spiritual growth and the intimacy in your marriage. Some assignments are Action Plans, Intimacy Conferences, *Sexperimenting* Techniques, etc.

❦ **Model Prayers.** Prayers are based on the Word of God for you to pray about any challenges you may have, and also include prayers of thanksgiving, repentance and renewal, etc.

❦ **Questions and Answers.** Some questions require a written response. You may consider some questions personal; therefore, if others have access to your Workbook, you may choose to not write out your responses. However, it is imperative for you to think through your answers to these questions.

❧ **Questions to Make You Think.** There are some questions where space is not provided for your written response. These thought-provoking questions are designed to direct you to focus on your personal circumstances.

So get ready to *work* your way to a lifetime of *Sexplosions!*

~ *Part I* ~

Abiding

1

Abide in the Word

What does abiding in the Word have to do with *sexplosion in marriage*? Everything! You can only *sexplode* when you ABIDE IN THE WORD. **This is the most important chapter in the Workbook and is the foundation for all the other chapters**. Only through abiding in the Word can you reap a bountiful harvest of *sexplosions* with your husband. If you do not apply the biblical principles of God's Word, you will not *sexperience sexhilarating sexplosions*. So, you must abide in the Word to experience an abundant life of sexual pleasures.

THE FOUNDATION

WOW, SEXPLOSION! Why such a straightforward, bold, and powerful title for a Christian book? Why should sexual intimacy be spoken of as less than straightforward, bold, and powerful? Why be ashamed or embarrassed to rejoice about the gift of sexual intimacy that God has given to the husband and wife in a covenant relationship with Him? The answer is simple: many wives do not receive sexual intimacy as a good and perfect gift from God, and secondly, many have believed the countless lies of Satan.

Lovemaking is a good and perfect gift from God to you and your husband. "Every good thing given and every perfect gift is from above, coming down from the Father of lights" (James 1:17). Satan's job is to kill, steal, and destroy everything God has designed as good and to be enjoyed (John 10:10). Satan seeks to kill, steal, and destroy the gift of lovemaking in many ways. Some ways, not all inclusive, are negative views of sex, wrong parental teaching, traumatic sexual experiences, disharmony in the marriage, being drawn away by lust into ungodly sexual practices or relationships, and for so many wives, a lack of knowledge of "how to" make love.

Get ready to change your life, thus your marriage, thus your marriage bed. But, to do so, you have to put first things first. There is no *sexplosion* unless you put all of the ingredients together. Consider when you make a cake, you must first make sure you have some flour. Then you mix in all the other ingredients. It is only after you have baked it that you can put the topping on. That's similar to experiencing *sexplosion in marriage:* it requires putting first things first, and that is to first abide in the Word of God, and only then can you enjoy the topping of *sexplosive* lovemaking.

FIRST THINGS FIRST

A marriage that does not have Christ as the foundation will be void of all the blessings God designed for marriage, including *sexplosions.* To obtain the blessings of a *sexplosive* marriage requires you to put first things first. In Matthew 6:33, "all things" include, but are not limited to, enjoying intimacy with your husband, achieving victory over strongholds, producing an abundant harvest of good fruit, and experiencing complete joy in marriage. The most profound aspect of Matthew 6:33 is the foundation. The foundation is Christ *and* His righteousness.

Abide in the Word

"But seek first His kingdom *and* His righteousness, and all these things will be added to you."

Matthew 6:33 (emphasis added)

That which is holy and right must come first, then *"all things"* will indeed come later.

Frequently people say Christ is first and they are seeking what is right and holy, yet their actions do not agree with their words. Do you say Christ is first and you are seeking His kingdom first? Is there a contradiction in what you say and the fruit produced in your marriage? Look at your marriage and determine if Christ is really first in every aspect. Are you seeking His righteousness—that which is holy and right? Only through abiding in the Word can these questions be answered. The fifteenth chapter of the gospel of John and the first epistle of John are good places to begin to evaluate what is first in your life. Why should you begin with these two studies? They command you to abide in the Word and for His words to abide in you. If you abide in the Word and let His words abide in you, your marriage will portray the abundant fruit of His righteousness. Placing Christ first through abiding in His Word will be evident in every aspect of your marriage.

MEANING OF "ABIDE"

To answer truthfully whether or not you are abiding requires you to have a biblical understanding of abiding. There are four Greek words for *abide*. *Strong's Exhaustive Concordance of the Bible* outlines the following Greek meanings of the word *abide:* *Mĕnō* is to exhort us to abide in Christ; to stay (in a given place or relation or expectancy); abide; continue; dwell; endure; be present; remain. *Ĕpimĕnō* is to remain, to tarry, to abide, to continue. *Paramĕnō* is to stay near; be permanent; continue; abide. *Prŏsmĕnō* is to cleave unto, adhere, abide still, continue with, remain in a place with a person.

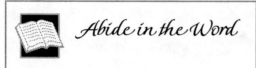

Abide in the Word

If you want to experience sexplosion in your marriage you must ABIDE IN THE WORD.

Merriam-Webster Online Collegiate® Dictionary (© 2002) defines *abide* as "to wait for (await); to endure without yielding (withstand); to bear patiently (tolerate) to accept without objection"; "to remain stable or fixed in a state; to continue in a place"; and "abide by; to conform to; to acquiesce in."

MEANING OF "WORDS"

In John 15:7, "words" refers to His commands, His utterances, and His teachings.

PUT IT ALL TOGETHER

God commands you to remain, stay, continue, be steadfast, endure, be tenacious, be persistent, be immovable, adhere, and be permanent in Him and in His teachings, commands, and sayings. Abiding in God's Word will allow you to be free to enjoy all the blessings of sexual intimacy. God's freedom is experienced only when you know what He teaches about sexual intimacy. God's Word says His people perish for a lack of knowledge. Is your marriage perishing? Is your marriage bed perishing? Abide in His Word and receive His abundant blessings in your life, your marriage, and indeed your marriage bed.

BLESSINGS AND EVIDENCES OF ABIDING IN THE WORD

How do you know if you are abiding in Him and His teachings are abiding in you? Only through believing the Scriptures can the truth of this matter be resolved. Some of the marital blessings and evidences of abiding in the Word are:

Answered Prayer
(Study John 15:7)

Jesus says, "*If* you abide in Me, and My words abide in you, ask whatever you wish, and it will be done for you" (emphasis added). Do you believe Jesus would lie? Do you believe He will do what He says He will do? *No*, He does not lie (Numbers 23:19). *Yes*, Jesus will do what He says He will do (Isaiah 46:11; Jeremiah 1:12). Your answers to your prayers are not about Jesus coming through, but about you abiding. What you must do is ABIDE in Him! When the Word abides in you, you have faith (Matthew 21:21–22)! When the Word abides in you, you will ask and receive (Matthew 7:7–8). Evidence of abiding is answered prayer. Abide in Him and His words in you and make your specific requests known to Him about how you can have *sexplosive* intimacy.

Fruitfulness
(Study John 15:4–5)

When you go to shop for fruit, you do not pick up any fruit. You inspect them for fruit flies, spots, bruises, and other blemishes.

When was the last time you checked the fruit you are producing in your marriage? Instead of checking your own fruit, let God check them for you. If you are abiding, then you have His Spirit (1 John 4:13). If you have His Spirit, you will produce the fruit of the Spirit, not the fruit of the flesh (Romans 8:4). Romans 8:6–9 says *"if"* you are of Christ, then your mind is set on spiritual things, not things (fleshly) that are hostile toward God. If you are in the flesh, you cannot please God. Are your fruit of the flesh or of His Spirit? What would your husband say? Or better yet, what would God say? If you are abiding in the Word, then you should be bearing fruit of encouragement, peace, kindness, and love, all of which would bless your husband.

Flesh Fruit (Not Abiding)	Spirit Fruit (Abiding)
Strife	Harmony
Hatred	Love
Outbursts of Anger	Soft, Gentle Answer
Pride/Selfishness	Humble Spirit
Rudeness	Respectful

1. What blessing is mentioned in John 15:11?

    _____

    _____

    _____

2. In relation to the blessing in John 15:11, according to John 16:22, can the world or your husband take this blessing away?
    ❏ Yes   ❏ No

True Discipleship
(Study John 15:8; John 8:31–32)

1. What is a disciple?

_____

_____

According to John 15:8 and John 8:31, Jesus clearly states in this conditional statement, *"if"* you abide in His Word, *"then"* you are true disciples.

2. Are you abiding in the teachings of Christ (2 John 9)?
   ❏ Yes   ❏ No

3. What additional evidence does John 13:35 give for being Jesus' true disciple?

_____

_____

_____

4. What evidence of abiding is indicated in John 15:14?

_____

_____

_____

5. This blessing is presented as a condition—*"if"* you do what?

_____

_____

Glorifying God (Study John 15:8 and Romans 15:1–7)

1. What does "glorify" mean?

_____

_____

_____

2. How can you glorify God in your marriage?

_____

_____

_____

_____

Freedom (Study John 8:31–32)

"If" you are abiding in the Word, then you are a true disciple. True disciples know the truth. His Word is truth (John 17:17). Only true disciples know the truth and are therefore free from the bondage of sin. Are you experiencing freedom over the bondage of pornography, sexual lust, sexual masturbation of self without the spouse, fear of "letting go" sexually, being naked and unashamed, negative communication, stress/fatigue, and other hindrances to your intimacy with God and your husband?

Love Demonstrated (Study 1 John 3:14–18; John 13:34–45)

A true disciple loves, just as Christ loved. You cannot say you love God if you neglect, deprive, abuse, ridicule, disrespect, and degrade your husband (1 John 4:20). A true disciple demonstrates love by giving to and serving her husband, just as Christ gave to and served you. When you abide in the Word, you demonstrate love by giving blessings, instead of curses, when wrongs are done to you (1 Corinthians 13:5). You demonstrate love to your husband by being kind and not rude (1 Corinthians 13:4–5). Are you demonstrating love in action, not just in words, toward your husband (1 John 3:18)?

Walking as Jesus Walked (Study 1 John 2:6)

To walk, meaning to follow and live as Jesus walked, you must know how He walked. Your abiding in the Word is evidenced when you imitate His walk, speech, actions, and character. If you are abiding, then you are walking: in love that is self-sacrificing (1 John 3:17; Ephesians 5:2); in forgiveness (Ephesians 4:29–32); in unselfishness (Philippians 2:3–4); in doing good (1 Peter 3:13); in obedience (1 John 3:24); and in the Spirit and not in the flesh (Romans 8:5–14; Galatians 5:19–23).

Obedience (Study 1 John 2:3–5; 1 John 5:3; John 15:10; John 14:15,21, 23, 24)

Your abiding in the Word is evident by your obedience to God's commands. Are you obedient to the following commands of God, in regard to your marriage?

Loving your husband (John 15:15,17;
John 13:34–35; 1 John 4:7–21; Titus 2:4) ❑ Yes ❑ No

Pursuing peace toward your husband
(Romans 12:18) ❑ Yes ❑ No

Forgiving your husband for wrongs he
has done (Ephesians 4:32) ❑ Yes ❑ No

Being kind toward him (Ephesians 4:32) ❏ Yes ❏ No

Being devoted to him (Romans 12:10) ❏ Yes ❏ No

Honoring and respecting your husband
(Ephesians 5:33) ❏ Yes ❏ No

Not depriving or withholding sex
(1 Corinthians 7:1–5) ❏ Yes ❏ No

Sowing a blessing instead of returning evil
for evil or insult for insult (1 Peter 3:9–11) ❏ Yes ❏ No

Being naked and unashamed with your
husband (Genesis 2:25) ❏ Yes ❏ No

Submitting to proper family order: husband,
then children (Matthew 5:6; Titus 2:4) ❏ Yes ❏ No

Allowing your husband's needs and interests to
be greater than your own (Philippians 2:3–4) ❏ Yes ❏ No

Not being overcome by stress, and fear
(Isaiah 26:3; Philippians 4:6–7) ❏ Yes ❏ No

Eternal Life
(Study 2 John 9; Also read John 17:3; 1 John 5:11, 20; 1 John 2:24–25)

1. According to 2 John 9, how is it evident if you have the Father and the Son?

_____

_____

Abide in the Word

> "Anyone who goes too far and does *not* abide in the teaching of Christ, does *not* have God; the one who abides in the teaching, he has both the Father and the Son."
> 2 John 9 (emphasis added)

2. If you say you know the *"teachings of Christ,"* what are His teachings as they relate to marriage, including sexual intimacy?

_____

_____

_____

3. What is the evidence in your marriage that you are abiding in the "teachings of Christ"?

_____

_____

Evidences of Eternal Life

If you are abiding in the teachings of Christ, it will be evident in your life. If you are abiding in the teachings of Christ, you have an eternal relationship with God the Father and with Jesus Christ, God's only begotten Son. The evidence provided in God's Word will aid you in determining whether or not you are abiding in His teachings; thus you have eternal life. The evidence for identifying your eternal relationship with Him is through your knowing Him, your faith, your fruit, and your belief.

Eternal Life Is Evidenced By Knowing God

Do you know Him? How do you know Him? What knowledge do you have of Him? Do you know about Him intellectually or doctrinally, or do you really know Him through having an intimate, committed relationship with Him?

Eternal Life Is Evidenced By Your Faith

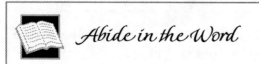 *Abide in the Word*

What is Eternal Life? Eternal life is evidenced by your abiding in the Word. *"This is eternal life,* that they may **know** You, the only true God, and Jesus Christ whom You have sent." John 17:3 (emphasis added)

If you know Him, which is eternal life (John 17:3), it will be evident by your faith in Him. Your faith goes beyond knowing who He is and His attributes. Your faith acts upon developing intimacy with Him to personally *know* Him through trusting Him, spending time with Him, allowing Him to be in complete control of you, and freely giving of yourself to please Him. You can intimately *know* God only when you abide in Him.

Eternal Life Is Evidenced By Your Fruit

If you know Him, which is eternal life (John 17:3), it will be evident by your fruit. You will produce a harvest of either good or bad fruit (Matthew 7:15–23; Matthew 12:33–37). What fruit are you producing? You cannot produce both good *and* bad fruit. Check the vine that abides in you. What vine dwells within you? You are either in the Vine, Jesus Christ, or not in the Vine (John 15:4–5).

If you are producing fruit because of the seed of the Holy Spirit being rooted in you, you will yield a bountiful harvest of blessings in your marriage. The fruit of your life should mirror

Abide in the Word

"You do not have His word abiding in you, for you do not **believe** Him whom He sent."
John 5:38 (emphasis added)

the One you are in union with, Jesus Christ. *"If"* you are in the vine of Christ and He is in you, your marriage should produce the fruit of love, peace, joy, harmony, kindness, gentleness, and all that Christ portrayed (Galatians 5:22–23).

However, if you are producing bad fruit, be not deceived, for God is not mocked (Galatians 6:7). If you are sowing evil and corrupt seed, then you are reaping evil and corrupt fruit. This does not lead to eternal life. God will declare, "I never *knew* you; depart from Me" (Matthew 7:23, emphasis added). What fruit do you see in your marriage? Do you find sinful anger, bitterness, discontentment, unforgiveness, pride, selfishness, and other fruit that Christ does not exemplify?

Eternal Life Is Evidenced By Your Belief

If you know Him, which is eternal life (John 17:3), it will be evident by your belief in Him. *Strong's Exhaustive Concordance* defines *believe* as: to inwardly rely on for salvation; agree; assure; faith; have confidence; obey; trust; yield; to entrust one's spiritual well being to Christ.

If you are not abiding in Him and He is not abiding in you, you have not committed yourself to Christ. If you do not believe in Him, this is why you are not abiding in Him (John 5:38). This is a damnable eternal state, in which you should not be content or complacent.

"Playing church," "being religious," "going through the motions of being a Christian, a false disciple," or "being lukewarm" is not abiding in Christ. If this is your situation, stop the deception. God knows your heart, and He will not commit Himself to you until you are sincere in heart and choose to believe on Him, evidenced through abiding In Him. "But Jesus, on His part, was not entrusting Himself to them, for He knew all men," (John 2:24).

No Evidence of *Abiding*

If there is no evidence of you abiding in the Word and the Word abiding in you (John 15:7), the first thing you must do is get to know the Greatest Lover. The only way to experience the blessings of Christ, including lasting, ongoing, consistent *sexplosions* in marriage, is to experience a relationship with the Greatest Lover, Jesus Christ. No Jesus, no love! Know Jesus, know love!

MEET THE LOVER

If you are not *abiding in the Word,* you do not know **The Lover**. If you do not know **The Lover**, you cannot understand or experience dynamic, *sexplosive* love. Abide in the love of **The Lover** and love Him and you can have *sexplosive* love with your husband. You must first experience spiritual intimacy with God to experience relationship intimacy with your husband.

WHO IS THIS GREAT LOVER?

He is none other than God Almighty (1 John 4:8, 16). The Bible teaches that God loves you and wants you to know Him: "Who desires all men to be saved and to come to the knowledge of the truth" (1 Timothy 2:4).

But you are separated from God and His love. Why? Because every person has sinned against God! "But your iniquities have made a separation between you and your God, and your sins have hidden His face from you so that He does not hear" (Isaiah 59:2).

By sinning, you separate yourself from God: "Being darkened in their understanding, excluded from the life of God because of the ignorance that is in them, because of the hardness of their heart" (Ephesians 4:18).

Where does this separation from God lead you? This separation from God brings everlasting death and punishment: "When the Lord Jesus will be revealed from heaven with His mighty angels in flaming fire, dealing out retribution to those who do not know God and to those who do not obey the gospel of our Lord Jesus. These will pay the penalty of eternal destruction, away from the presence of the Lord and from the glory of His power" (2 Thessalonians 1:7–9).

There is only ONE solution. God, in His great love for you, sent His only begotten Son, Jesus Christ, to earth to bear the burden and punishment of your sins. Jesus came and lived on earth as your example of righteous living (1 Peter 2:21–22). He suffered a brutal, horrific death on a cross so that your sins might be forgiven and you could be restored unto God (1 Peter 3:18). Jesus did not stay dead; God raised Him again and He now sits in Heaven on the right hand of God (1 Corinthians 15:3–4; Hebrews 1:3; 10:12). "For God so loved the world, that He gave His only begotten Son, that whoever believes in Him shall not perish, but have eternal life" (John 3:16). "He made Him who knew no sin *to be* sin on our behalf, so that we might become the righteousness of God in Him" (2 Corinthians 5:21, emphasis added).

HOW CAN YOU PERSONALLY ACCEPT THIS GREAT LOVER?

By accepting Jesus Christ as your personal Savior and Lord.

> **A**cknowledge that you are a sinner, separated eternally from God. Acknowledge that you need the only Savior, Jesus Christ, to save you from eternal separation from God (Romans 6:23; 3:23; John 3:15–16; John 20:31).
> **B**elieve in your heart that God has raised Jesus from the dead (Romans 10:9; Acts 16:31; 1 Corinthians 15:3–4).
> **C**onfess with your mouth that Jesus is your Lord (Romans 10:9).

HOW DO YOU GET TO KNOW THIS LOVER BETTER?

Abide in the Word! Study His Word! Believe the Word! Obey His Word! "Grow in the grace and knowledge of our Lord and Savior Jesus Christ" (2 Peter 3:18). To be committed and faithful to grow in the knowledge of Jesus, helpful resources are provided in this Workbook. Refer to *"Tips for Developing and Implementing an Action Plan,"* Appendix A; the *"Accountability Spiritual Support Partner Guidelines,"* Appendix B; and the additional spiritual growth resources listed in Appendix C.

Prayer of Salvation

God,

I agree that I have sinned and am separated from You (Romans 3:23; Romans 6:23). Thank you for taking the punishment of my sins when Your Son, Jesus Christ, suffered and died on the cross. Please forgive me of my sin and cleanse me from all that is not right in me (1 John 1:9). I receive Jesus Christ, Your gift of Love, into my heart and life as my Lord and Savior (Romans 10:9, 10, 13). I choose this day to abide in Your teachings so that I may intimately know You (John 15:7; John 17:3; 2 John 9). Thank You for my salvation.

In Jesus' Name I pray,
Amen

If you prayed this prayer and accepted Jesus Christ as your personal Lord and Savior today, please notify us at www.abideintheword.org. We would like to send you additional information about your new life in Christ Jesus and how you can know God in a more intimate way.

HOW TO ABIDE IN THE WORD

A*bide in the word through being committed to*
B*ible study, prayer, and fasting;*
I *nvesting in your spiritual growth;*
D*eveloping action plans and accountability/spiritual*
  support partners; and living an
E *xchanged life that glorifies God.*

Upon accepting Jesus Christ as Lord and Savior of your life, you must surrender every aspect of your life to walk as He walked. Now that you understand God's command *to* abide in Him, here are a few practical tips for *how* to abide. Apply these tips to abide in the Word and experience complete and full joy in your life, and a harvest of blessings in your marriage.

ABIDE

As outlined in *"The Foundation"* section of chapter 1, "abide" is to remain, to stay, and to continue in the Word of God. Remaining in the Word is permanent regardless of any circumstances in your life or what your husband does or does not do for you. You may feel as if that is impossible, yet God has made all things possible for those who believe (Luke 18:27). God has made everything possible and has given you the teachings in His Word to equip you to be victorious in all things. To abide in the Word, you must know and obey His Word.

BIBLE STUDY AND PRAYER

To walk just as He walked, you must know how He walked (1 John 2:6). You know how He walked by getting to know Him. The way you get to know Him is through spending quality intimate time with Him through studying His teachings and talking to Him through prayer and fasting. As you develop a deep intimate relationship with God, you are transformed to be like Him in words and deeds (1 John 3:18).

Bible Study

You get to enjoy true intimacy with your husband only after you have known true intimacy with God. True intimacy with God is developed through spending quality time with Him. You spend quality intimate time with God through studying His Word. Learn how to study the Word of God, then *study!* Where do you begin? Begin with having a detailed, comprehensive Bible study on the topic of *"Abiding in the Word."* Why do you begin with a Bible study on *abiding in the Word?* As you begin to apply the biblical *sexplosion* principles, a study of abiding in the Word will encourage and teach you:

- ❦ Knowledge of what God's Word says (Psalm 119; John 8:32).
- ❦ Obedience to keep God's words (1 John 2:3).
- ❦ Analysis of self to see yourself through God's Word (2 Timothy 2:15).
- ❦ Steadfastness to stand firm in the Word of God when you encounter trials, temptations, struggles, and doubts (2 Timothy 3:16).
- ❦ Freedom to enjoy sexual intimacy and freedom over inhibitions (John 8:31–32).
- ❦ Liberty to know what is acceptable or unacceptable in the marriage bed (Hebrews 13:4).
- ❦ The "golden rule" principle to know whether or not you can say "no" to your husband's sexual requests when you are tired, or you are not desirous, or you are too busy (Luke 6:31).
- ❦ The ability to overcome the challenges of past sexual relationships or experiences (1 John 2:14).

Some helpful spiritual growth resources on studying the Bible are listed in Appendix C.

Praying and Fasting

"And whatever we ask we receive from Him, because we keep His commandments and do the things that are pleasing in His sight" (1 John 3:22). Prayer is communion with God. As God talks to you through His Word, you must talk with Him through prayer. God's Word teaches you how to pray about every aspect of your marriage. Be diligent and committed to abide in the Word. Here are some practical biblical tips for praying and fasting about your marriage:

- 🌺 When you pray, make your specific requests known to Him in faith (Philippians 4:6; Matthew 21:21–22).
- 🌺 Pray without ceasing (Ephesians 6:18; 1 Thessalonians 5:17).
- 🌺 Pray for your husband if he is spiteful (Matthew 5:44).
- 🌺 Pray and do not lose heart. Do not give in; do not have doubt, fear, or unbelief; and do not be discouraged (Luke 18:1).
- 🌺 Pray according to God's will, which is knowing what He says (1 John 5:14).
- 🌺 Maintain harmony, because discord hinders prayers (1 Peter 3:7).
- 🌺 Fast, as needed. In particular, fast when you are dealing with obstacles that are stubborn and resistant to change, and when you do not seem to be making progress (Matthew 17:21; Mark 9:29).

Some helpful spiritual growth resources on praying and fasting are listed in Appendix C.

INVEST IN YOUR SPIRITUAL GROWTH

Making a commitment to abide in the Word requires you to invest in your spiritual growth. Set aside specific dedicated time for your personal study time in God's Word. For your personal study time, invest in spiritual growth resources that will aid in your study of the Word. Recommended resources are a Bible dictionary, a collegiate dictionary, a concordance, a parallel study Bible, Bible study software, this Workbook, marriage enrichment books, etc.

Attend marriage workshops, retreats, etc. When appropriate, obtain marriage counseling. Participate in a Christian-based small group Bible study that believes the Holy Bible to be without error and inspired by God. Be a doer and not just a hearer of these biblical *sexplosion* principles outlined in this Workbook. Be aggressive to develop and implement an **Action Plan** for how you will abide in the biblical *sexplosion* principles outlined in this Workbook. For *"Tips for Developing and Implementing An Action Plans,"* refer to Appendix A.

DEVELOP ACCOUNTABILITY/SPIRITUAL SUPPORT PARTNER (ASSP) RELATIONSHIPS

Whenever you seek to make lifestyle changes or commitments to enhance your marriage, you will always find obstacles that will hinder you from carrying out your desires. As you make a commitment to abide in the Word and to adhere to the biblical *sexplosion* principles in this Workbook, you will need someone to hold you accountable, exhort you, teach you, rebuke you, pray with you, and give you godly counsel. The most effective way to do this is to obtain a mentor or an Accountability/Spiritual Support Partner (ASSP). A few biblical principles for an ASSP are:

- She is to lift you up (Ecclesiastes 4:9–10).
- Older women are to teach the younger (Titus 2:4–5).
- You are to restore one another (Galatians 6:1).
- She is to cheer you up when you feel like all hope is gone (Proverbs 12:25).

Guidelines on developing and maintaining an ASSP are listed in Appendix B.

EXCHANGED LIFE

Questions

- 🌸 *How do you live a committed life of obedience to the Word of God?*
- 🌸 *How do you consistently apply these biblical sexplosion principles?*
- 🌸 *How do you not lose heart in doing good to your husband, when he does not reciprocate the good done to him?*
- 🌸 *How can you always give and give and give day in and day out, over and over again?*
- 🌸 *How can you not allow past wrongs done to you not control your actions and thoughts?*
- 🌸 *How can you stop struggling with weight, self-image, sinful anger, and bitterness?*

Answer

The answer to these questions is to experience an *Exchanged life* through Christ Jesus. What does an *Exchanged life* mean? It simply means to make an exchange from living in the flesh to living in the Spirit of Christ Jesus. You must stop trusting in yourself and put your total faith and trust in what God has done for you through Christ Jesus. You believe and act on God's Word that says, *"I have been crucified with Christ; and it is no longer I who live, but Christ lives in me"* (Galatians 2:20(a)).

You must allow Christ to live in and through you. If you are a Christian, a follower of Jesus Christ, your old sinful, evil, negative, hateful, unproductive life was crucified when Christ was crucified on the cross (Romans chapters 6, 7, and 8). As a Christian, you have a new spirit-filled life of joy, peace, love, kindness, and gentleness. You should live the *exchanged life* of Christ living in you. The exchanged life is alive in you, so then you are acting, talking, and walking like Christ (1 John 2:5–6).

If there are areas in your marriage where it is evident you are not allowing Christ to be alive in you, make a commitment to:

- ♥ *Exchange* your old *way of living* for a new way in Christ Jesus (2 Corinthians 5:17; Ephesians 4:24).
- ♥ *Exchange* what you used to do in *your own strength* and might for doing what God requires through His strength and might (Zechariah 4:6).
- ♥ *Exchange* your *serving* out of obligation for serving out of love (Romans 15:7; John 3:16).
- ♥ *Exchange* your *"what about me" attitude* for the sacrificial giving attitude of Christ (Philippians 2:5–8).
- ♥ *Exchange* any wrong *beliefs* to agree with the Word of God. Agree with God that you are dead to and freed from sin (Romans 6:7, 11, 18); you are no longer a slave to sin (Romans 6:6); and no sin or stronghold shall master you (Romans 6:9, 14).

To learn more about what the exchanged life is, what you are exchanging, and how to make the exchange, refer to Appendix C for information on the Exchanged Life Ministries.

Applying the five A.B.I.D.E. principles to abide in the Word are foundational to having a *sexplosive* marital relationship. Apart from Christ you can do nothing (John 15:4–5). Abiding in the Word provides victory over all hindrances and inhibitions to *sexplosive* sexual intimacy.

2

Hindrances to Sexual Intimacy

*W*ives encounter many hindrances to their sexual intimacy. The roots of these hindrances are varied in cause. Some root causes may be health related and others sin related. Whatever the cause, it must be identified and resolved so it may no longer hinder you from *sexperiencing* a lifetime of *sexhilarating sexplosions*.

HINDRANCES TO SEXUAL INTIMACY

Sex therapists and medical experts report the following, not all-inclusive, to have an effect on sexual intimacy. Many may either be sin, or an ill effect as a result of sin, or improper teaching, or the evidence of a medical, physical, or psychological condition.

EMOTIONAL-PSYCHOLOGICAL
(Circle the ones that hinder you)

- 💗 Emotional or psychological hindrances may include: being overwhelmed with the stresses of life, the death of a loved one within the last six months, the loss of a job within the last year, financial setbacks, relocating to a new city, lifestyle time constraints, children, stresses of parenting, a lack of privacy, a lack of sexual knowledge or of *how to* make love, or a lack of sexual confidence.
- 💗 Inhibitions or mental obstacles that may hinder you: false beliefs about sex, including *do's and don'ts, rights and wrongs, "good girls don't."*
- 💗 Marital relationship hindrances may be: an emotional disconnection from your husband, sinful anger, bitterness, unforgiveness, sexual rejection by your husband, emotional or sexual infidelity, boredom with routine intimacy, or lack of romance.
- 💗 Fears that may hinder you: *"letting go"* or appearing *"wild,"* making noise while making love, being sexually misunderstood, being pregnant, having sex, etc.
- 💗 Self-image perception hindrances may be: being insecure in your physical appearance, or feeling incomplete as a result of a hysterectomy or a mastectomy.
- 💗 Traumatic sexual experience hindrances may be as a result of: rape, incest, molestation, abortion, prostitution, etc.

PHYSICAL
(Circle the ones that hinder you)

❧ Health-related conditions that may hinder your sexual desire or pleasure: pregnancy, constipation, diabetes, kidney or thyroid abnormalities, anemia, heart disease, cancer, autoimmune diseases, a prolapsed uterus, urine leakage, nervous system disorders, fatigue, low energy, or hormonal fluctuation related to menopause, hysterectomy, premenstrual symptoms, etc.

❧ Pain-related conditions that can negatively impact your desire: endometriosis, infection of the bladder (cystitis), pelvic tumors, a congenital abnormality, radiation therapy for cancer, infections of the cervix or fallopian tubes, episiotomy, surgery resulting in a narrowing of the vagina, swelling of the glands along the vaginal opening known as v*estibulitis,* vaginal dryness, pain on entry, a involuntary tightening of the vaginal muscles or an unconscious desire to prevent penetration during intercourse known as *vaginismus,* painful intercourse known as *dyspareunia,* inflammation and infection of the vagina known as *vaginitis,* or allergic reaction as a result of vaginal douches, deodorants, bath additives, nonoxynol–9 spermicides, or other factors, etc.

❧ Medications that may hinder your desire: heartburn remedies, some birth control pills, ulcer medicines, antidepressants, blood pressure drugs, cholesterol prescriptions, tranquilizers, and sleeping pills. Substances that dry mucus membranes: asthma drugs, antihistamines, diuretics, alcohol, caffeine, etc.

Consult with your personal physician or gynecologist regarding health-related concerns. Additional resources are listed in Appendix C.

SPIRITUAL
(Circle the ones that hinder you)

❧ Hindrances listed here are most often sin related: current or past sexual immoral acts or lascivious behavior, masturbation of self (without your husband present), neglecting or withholding sex from your husband, faking orgasms, fantasy or lust, pornography, or using sex as a bargaining tool or for penalization.

There are many hindrances to sexual intimacy. It is imperative for you to stop and identify what hinders you and why.

MAKE IT PERSONAL

The following assignment is for you to identify your own sexual intimacy hindrances. Pray and ask God to reveal to you all that hinder your sexual intimacy. List them with "1" being the greatest.

1. _____

2. _____

3. _____

4. _____

5. _____

6. _____

7. _____

Pray and ask God to reveal to you the *root cause,* meaning the reason of each hindrance you listed above. Write out the root cause of each one.

1. _____

2. _____

3. _____

4. _____

5. _____

6. _____

7. _____

A CLOSER LOOK AT YOUR LIFE

Take a closer look at your life regarding any sexual hindrances or challenges that may inhibit you from freely enjoying sexual intimacy to the fullest extent God desires for you. This section provides a summation of various sexual hindrances, the consequences of these hindrances, and the teaching of God's Word to offer you His freedom. If these hindrances apply to you and the consequences are affecting you, do not disregard them or procrastinate in addressing them. Choose right now to receive the victory through Christ Jesus when you abide in the Word, His commands.

SEX OUTSIDE OF THE MARRIAGE BED

Sex outside of the marriage bed may include, but is not limited to, homosexuality, orgies or group sex, animals (bestiality), fantasy, any type of non-intercourse with another (e.g., oral, manual stimulation, internet sex, etc.). Participating in any form of sex that is not exclusively between you and your husband is sin and hinders the marital relationship. Have you been or are you getting your sexual desires fulfilled from something or someone other than your husband?

Consequences

The consequence or result of such sin opens the door for Satan to attack your sexually deprived husband (1 Corinthians 7:5). This is disobedience to God because you have sexually neglected your husband (1 Corinthians 7:1–5). God will judge fornicators and adulterers (Hebrews 13:4). This unrepentant lifestyle will result in eternal separation from God (1 Corinthians 6:9–10; Galatians 5:19–21; Revelation 21:8; Revelation 22:14–15).

The end result of sex outside of the marriage covenant leads to guilt, condemnation, and lack of trust. If you were engaged in sex before marriage, you may feel guilty and believe God condemns you. You may not trust your husband because you have the idea that if he had sex with you before you were married, he might commit other sexual sins while married to you. Satan will use your sinful actions as an opportunity to play rewind in your memory bank. If allowed, Satan will bring to your memory all the sexual sins (often called "fun" or "good") you had before marriage. If you allow him, Satan will make comparisons between your husband and other sinful sex relationships you had.

Commands of God (Abide in the Word)

You can experience freedom from this hindrance and all its ugly consequences. The freedom God gives is for you to know the marriage bed is the union of the husband and wife to receive pleasure from each other and none other (1 Corinthians 7:1–5). You do not have to allow this hindrance to continue to affect you. Come boldly before God's throne of grace (Hebrews 4:16) to confess sins outside of the marriage bed and be forgiven. Confess your sin *now* (1 John 1:9).

SEXUAL LUST AND FANTASY

Sexual lust and fantasy can destroy the marriage bed. Sexual lust begins in your thoughts or mind. Jesus says, "Everyone who looks at a woman with lust for her has already committed adultery with her in his heart" (Matthew 5:28). If your desire for emotional intimacy is not fulfilled within the marriage, Satan will certainly find an old boyfriend, a co-worker, or someone who *appears* to be interested in you more than your husband, *seems* to be more understanding than your husband, listens to you more than your husband does, or is a better conversationalist than your husband.

Consequences

Beware, you may initially think there are no consequences or it is not a big issue. Do not be naïve; Satan has never played fair. There are many negative effects of lust or fantasy. Most often it begins with comparisons. When you lust or fantasize, it may cause you to compare your husband sexually or emotionally and even spiritually to someone else or a fantasy person. You may have sexual fantasies about someone else while being sexually intimate with your husband. Then there is the temptation. Temptation comes from wrong desires within you (James 1:14). Temptation can lead to evil actions. Evil thoughts can become evil actions: sin (Proverbs 4:23 NCV; James 1:15). Evil actions can result in destruction. Sin is crouching at your door and its desire is for you (Genesis 4:7; James 5:8). Beware! Lust and a given opportunity can be a destructive combination (John 10:10). God warns you that the next consequence is death. When lust is conceived, it gives birth to sin; and sin, when it is full-grown, brings forth death (James 1:15).

Commands of God (Abide in the Word)

When you begin to abide in the Word, you can be free from this death because Jesus came to give you life (John 10:10). You must begin to abide in the teachings of Christ and begin to walk in the spirit of self-control (Galatians 5:23). Take every thought captive to the obedience of Christ (2 Corinthians 10:5(b)). Focus your mind on thoughts that are true, honorable, of good repute, excellent, and worthy of praise (Philippians 4:8). Avoid the people you lust after or fantasize about. Avoid things that may spark the lust or fantasy such as soap operas, romance novels, or ungodly *girlfriend* talk (1 John 2:15–17). Repent, now, not later! Make a commitment to do away with the old sinful life.

SEXUAL ADDICTIONS

There are various forms of sexual addictions or bondages that all hinder you sexually because they are sin. A sexual addiction may be a complete obsession of pornographic material, masturbation of self without the spouse present, fantasy, cybersex (internet), and other sexually immoral things. The following definitions are taken from *Merriam-Webster Online Collegiate® Dictionary,* © 2002:

- ❦ *Bestiality.* "Sexual relations between a human being and an animal." Sex with animals is outside of the marriage bed. God designed sex for the husband and wife and not with animals.
- ❦ *Masturbation* (of self without the spouse). "Erotic stimulation especially of one's genital organs commonly resulting in orgasm and achieved by manual or other bodily contact exclusive of sexual intercourse." It is sexually gratifying self. Sex is to be enjoyed between the husband and wife, not to exclude the other.
- ❦ *Pornography.* "Depiction of erotic behavior (and/or material) *intended* to cause sexual excitement." This behavior and/or material may include but is not limited to nudity events and places; sex educational videos; computers (internet); sex telephone services; movies, television/cable shows, etc.

Consequences

Participating in these types of sinful behaviors can result in being a slave to the sin of sexual immorality. You are a slave to whatever controls you (Romans 6:16; 2 Peter 2:19). Guilt is also associated with this sin because it is often a private sex addiction. Although there is guilt, the sex stronghold is greater than a commitment to walk in victory. The addiction can cause you to neglect the sexual relationship between you and your husband. You may even begin to demand that your husband participate in sexual immoral deeds or some form of media under the pretense of improving your sexual relationship. This only opens the door for Satan to put you and your husband into deeper bondage to sin.

Commands of God (Abide in the Word)

If your computer, DVD/VCR, etc., is an open door for you to sin, pluck it out (Matthew 5:29–30). Go and sin no more, lest a worse thing comes upon you (John 5:14). Make a covenant with your eyes to not look at anything that will draw you away from what is right according to God (Job 31:1; Psalm 101:3). Avoid sexual immorality (1 Thessalonians 4:3). The chains of sin are broken and you have been set free (Romans 6:18, 22). You are dead to sin, and sin no longer has control over you (Romans 6). Take the door of escape that God has given you when you are tempted to sin (1 Corinthians 10:13). Know that the source of these evil desires is not from God (1 John 2:15–17). Do not allow sin to control your body any longer, do not give in to its sinful desires (Romans 6:6–12).

Refer to *"Is It Right or Is It Wrong"* in chapter 9 and to Appendix C for suggested resources for biblical help to overcome this stronghold.

FLIRTING WITH OTHERS

Flirting (as referred to in this section) is a form of seduction or a playful come-on, whether consciously or unconsciously, to someone other than your husband (Proverbs 7:21–27; Proverbs 2:16–20). You may flirt with others to spark jealousy or anger in your husband, either because you want him to know other men are interested in you or want your husband to pay more attention to you.

Consequences

The consequence of flirting often leads from one negative to other negative behaviors. Flirting can draw you away emotionally and sexually from your husband (1 Corinthians 7:5). It can lead to other sinful behaviors, such as lust, fantasy, and then adultery. It also may cause the man or men you are flirting with to become weak and stumble by fantasizing or lusting after you (Romans 14:13(b); Matthew 18:7(c)).

Commands of God (Abide in the Word)

To avoid the pitfalls of fantasizing or lusting, make a covenant with your husband and God not to look with lust upon another (Job 31:1). Be wise in your appearance and your conversations. Do not cause someone to stumble (Romans 14:21).

SEXUAL TRAUMAS
(Whether you are the victim or perpetrator)

Sexual traumatic experiences can affect a person spiritually, emotionally, sexually, and sometimes physically. The following definitions are taken from *Merriam-Webster Online Collegiate® Dictionary,* © 2002:

- ❦ *Incest.* "Sexual intercourse between persons so closely related that they are forbidden by law to marry; the statutory crime of such a relationship."
- ❦ *Molestation.* "To make annoying sexual advances to; especially: to force physical and usually sexual contact on."
- ❦ *Rape.* "An act or instance of robbing or despoiling or carrying away a person by force; a sexual intercourse with a woman by a man without her consent and chiefly by force or deception."

Consequences

The aftereffect of these traumatic occurrences may be misplaced guilt, shame, condemnation, and self-hatred because she feels she may have caused or could have prevented the violation. She experiences many emotional, sexual, and physical distresses (e.g., terror, nightmares, willful memory loss, distorted view of self, rejection, masturbation, etc.). The memory of the abuse often produces a spirit of fear, sinful anger, bitterness, and unforgiveness against the perpetrator, self, God, and others indirectly involved. Promiscuity may be manifested in her life if the perpetrator justified his or her actions as an expression of "love" for the victim. A person's coping mechanism may include other works of the flesh such as drugs, alcoholism, or occult activity. Same-sex violations usually open the door to homosexual fantasies or homosexual relationships. Due to the pain of the violation, a disdain or disinterest in sex may occur and this trauma may be manifested in the marriage bed. The pleasure of sexual intimacy may be hindered because of a negative sexual experience. The victim may have a lack of trust in God or a negative view of Him because she feels He allowed the wrongs to be done to her.

Commands of God (Abide in the Word)

Only Satan wants you to be continually traumatized by any such event. Satan knows that if you continue to focus on your past, you will not experience the victory you have in Christ Jesus. God sent His only Son, Jesus Christ, to heal you from the sins of this world. Be healed from the ill effects of sexual abuse through the blood of the Lamb, Jesus Christ (Revelation 12:11). Receive God's healing spiritually, emotionally, physically, and sexually (Psalm 30:2; Psalm 107:20). Forgive the perpetrator and do not seek revenge (Luke 23:34; Matthew 6:14–15; Romans 12:17–21). Trust in the Lord with all your heart (Proverbs 3:5–6). You must know and believe you are not destroyed (2 Corinthians 4:8–9). Do not allow Satan to keep you in the bondage of shame or fear (Job 11:15–16). It is through the

Word of God that you will find strength, so abide in the Word (Psalm 119:28). You know you are an overcomer when you can use a negative experience as a testimony to minister to others who may have been victims of sexual traumas. (Revelation 12:11).

ABORTION

(Herein defined as the voluntary termination of the life of an unborn child.) Emotional and physical experiences are a result of either being forced to or having voluntarily participated in the termination of a life.

Consequences

Often there is a struggle within the person's mind of knowing that her confessed sin has truly been forgiven by God. Additionally, the memory of the abortion procedure can be so traumatic that it affects a person's ability to be free to enjoy sex in marriage. The person may experience guilt and condemnation for murder. Guilt and condemnation may be a mental stronghold because of experiencing an abortion. The association of the abortion procedure may cause a person to be ashamed to expose her vaginal area to her husband.

Commands of God (Abide in the Word)

Confess your sins, and believe in your heart that Jesus has forgiven you (1 John 1:9). There is no condemnation for those who are in Christ Jesus (Romans 8:1–2). Do not allow Satan to condemn you; the blood of Christ Jesus cleanses you from all confessed sin. God delivers you from all of your troubles (Psalm 34:19). Forgive those whom you feel may have wronged or sinned against you (Ephesians 4:32; Mark 11:25). God heals you from all wounds and hurts you may have suffered (Psalm 147:3; Jeremiah 30:17). Accept that God has cast that sin as far as the east is from the west and will remember it no more (Psalm 103:12; Hebrews 8:12).

LIES/DECEITFULNESS

Have you faked orgasms or spoken falsely regarding enjoying sex? Being deceptive that your husband has been satisfying and fulfilling your sexual needs is a lie. God hates lying, which is sin (Proverbs 6:16; Proverbs 12:22). Lying is not edifying, honoring, or respecting your husband (Ephesians 4:29).

Consequences

One lie can lead to another lie. As a result, you have built your marriage bed based on deceit and lies. As a result of your lies, you have allowed your husband to believe he is *great* in the bed. Lies produce disunity and a lack of trust in marriage.

Commands of God (Abide in the Word)

You are called to speak the truth in love (Ephesians 4:15(a); Colossians 3:9). Stop lying about your sexual pleasure or lack of it. Encourage your husband as you teach him how to truly pleasure you sexually (Ephesians 4:25). Be a doer and not just a reader of these biblical *sexplosion* principles and begin to *sexperience sexciting, sexhilarating, sexplosive* lovemaking.

DEFRAUDING YOUR HUSBAND

Defrauding means to withhold or deny your husband sexual fulfillment. Have you defrauded your husband because you are often too tired, or you were sick or on your menstrual cycle, or as a form of punishment—he does not receive because of something he did or did not do—or as form of manipulation—he can receive if he does something for you?

Consequences

Dissension between you and your husband will occur because sexual desires are not being met. Resentment and bitterness can result toward your husband because he is not satisfying you sexually or emotionally. Depriving your husband can open the door for your husband to get his desires met separately from you, whether through masturbation of self or an adulterous relationship (1 Corinthians 7:5). You are disobedient to God when you choose to withhold, deprive, reject, or say "no" (for whatever reason) to your husband.

Commands of God (Abide in the Word)

Defrauding your husband of sexual intimacy is sin (1 Corinthians 7:5). You must discard whatever excuse or justification for your sinful action. Acknowledge, confess, and repent of the sin of depriving your husband (1 John 1:9)! Be obedient to God, go and sin no more (John 5:14)! Restore harmony where there is discord in the marriage (Romans 12:18).

NOT FOR PLEASURE OF THE WIFE

You may have been erroneously taught there is no pleasure in sex and your role is to lie still and moan and groan to imitate pleasure. Or perhaps, you have never experienced orgasmic pleasure and thus have come to believe only your husband is supposed to experience pleasure.

Consequences

As a result, when you and your husband are sexually intimate, your mind tends to drift away or you are thinking *hurry up and get finished*. If you have believed that sexual intimacy was for the sole pleasure of your husband, you focused on gratifying only him because you did not know God also designed sexual intimacy for your pleasure too.

Commands of God (Abide in the Word)

The hindrances to sexual intimacy can be addressed only when you ABIDE IN THE WORD.

Lovemaking is not just for the sole pleasure of your husband. It is to be enjoyed by both you and your husband. You must exchange your wrong teachings, thoughts, attitudes, and feelings from believing you are supposed to focus only on your husband's pleasure and not receive sexual pleasure and gratification. If you have been focusing only on giving pleasure, most likely sexual intimacy for you has become a chore, an unpleasant task, and a waste of time. Resentment can build up within you. You will not be able to make love mentally, if this has been your challenge. Do away with such falsehoods and put on the truth of God's Word: God designed sexual intimacy for your pleasure, too. God wants you to enjoy everything He created for you. Do not feel or believe sexual intimacy is not for your pleasure. Sexual intimacy is a blessing from God to you!

What is it that hinders you from freely enjoying sexual intimacy as God intended? You must address the root. As you identify the root, abide in the Word to be an overcomer so you can receive the blessings of *sexplosive* lovemaking. Appendix C (Notes and Suggested Readings) provides additional resources and sources for additional information on these hindrances.

3

Overcoming Hindrances

Jesus Came to Set the Captive Free! "The Spirit of the Lord is upon me; he has appointed me to preach Good News to the poor; he has sent me to heal the brokenhearted and to announce that captives shall be released and the blind shall see, that the downtrodden shall be freed from their oppressors, and that God is ready to give blessings to all who come to him." Luke 4:18 (TLB)

AN OVERCOMER

An overcomer is one who has repented, meaning she has turned away from sin and has renounced and made a clean break from Satan and all sinful strongholds in her life. A stronghold is anything or anyone that hinders you or keeps you in bondage from truly experiencing all the abundant sexual intimacy blessings God has for you to enjoy.

As you abide in the Word, the biblical tips in this chapter can help you to be set free so you can walk in victory over all strongholds. Agree with God—you are dead to sin (Romans 6). Do not give in to Satan. You must learn how to take back everything Satan has stolen from you. If you do not address these issues, you will allow them to have a vicious cycle or stronghold in your life. As long as you give Satan the right or permission, he will continue to torment you and steal, kill, and destroy all that is rightfully yours as a child of God. You must read the Word of God, study it, and obey it so you may know who you are in Christ and how to overcome all sexual hindrances and strongholds.

GET TO THE ROOT OF THE STRONGHOLD

As long as you do not pluck up the root, which is the foundational cause of the stronghold, and only look at the surface issues or the fruits, that stronghold will continue to keep you in bondage. You must get to the root of the stronghold. Pray and ask God to reveal to you the root cause of the stronghold. Identify how and when Satan came in and began to cause havoc. Put an end to Satan's havoc in your life by plucking the root, not just the fruit. You may need to seek wise godly counsel to help you identify the root cause of strongholds in your life.

ACKNOWLEDGE, CONFESS, REPENT, AND FORGIVE

First, you must acknowledge anything in your life that is not a characteristic of God. Confess and repent of those ungodly characteristics, which include bitterness, sinful anger, resentment, condemnation, worthlessness, doubt, unbelief, guilt, shame, hate, rage, death, destruction, unforgiveness, sexual sin, and remembrance of wrongs done to you and wrongs you have done to others.

Secondly, forgive those who have sinned against you (Matthew 6:12) and those you have anything against (Mark 11:25). Unforgiveness opens the door for all of its other negative and destructive friends to come into your life. The friends of unforgiveness are self-pity, hatred, sinful anger, resentment, criticism, bitterness, depression, and other tormenting problems (Matthew 18:21–35). If continual discord is between you and your spouse, you cannot experience *sexplosive* lovemaking. Do not allow pride and stubbornness keep you from forgiving your husband for wrongs he may have done to you. Do away with the sin of unforgiveness. God said that if you do not forgive, He would not forgive you (Matthew 6:14–15). Make a choice to forgive all who have sinned against you.

 *Abide in the Word*

1. What should you do with sin according to Proverbs 28:13?

_____

_____

_____

2. What should you do with sin according to Acts 26:20?

_____

_____

_____

RECEIVE GOD'S HEALING

Receive God's healing for yourself and receive healing for others who have sinned against you. Do not allow the perpetrator to keep you hostage, spiritually, mentally, or physically. Receive God's healing for bitterness, resentment, condemnation, worthlessness, doubt, guilt, shame, hate, rage, suicidal thoughts, sexual sins (whether victim or perpetrator), pre-marital sexual relationships, adultery, etc.

Abide in the Word

1. According to Luke 4:18, what has God done for you?

_____

_____

2. According to 2 Chronicles 7:14, what does God require of you?

_____

_____

_____

3. According to 2 Chronicles 7:14, what will God do for you?

_____

_____

_____

4. According to Psalm 34:18–20, what does God do for you?

_____

_____

_____

BREAK EVERY YOKE— BREAK UNGODLY SOUL TIES

Sin begets sin. Once it takes root in your life, it will continually reproduce itself within your life. For this reason, you must make a clean cut from the root foundation of all sin. You must be aggressive to disassociate yourself from sin or the entanglement of sin. Cancel out sin. Do not continue to allow sin to control your mind, thoughts, and actions. Have nothing to do with the connection of sin that would keep you in its control. Some practical ways to break ungodly soul ties such as sinful sexual relationships are:

- 💗 Pray against and close the door to sin. Stop allowing Satan to have rights to torment you in your life (Matthew 18:34–35).
- 💗 Claim God's Word that you are free through Christ Jesus from the bondage of all sin (Romans chapters 6–8).
- 💗 Renounce all association with ungodly relationships (soul ties): internet or cybersex, fantasies, the perpetra-

tor of an abusive relationship, pornography, adulterous and premarital sex relationships (1 Corinthians 6:16).

♥ Discard all material that maybe a stumbling block for you. Such material may include magazines, books, videos, pictures, and memorabilia of former boyfriends or sexual partners.

1. What does 2 Peter 2:20–22 teach about returning to a stronghold that Christ has freed you from?

_____

_____

_____

2. What does Proverbs 26:11 teach you regarding returning to a stronghold that Christ has freed you from?

_____

_____

_____

3. What did Christ do for you according to Galatians 5:1?

_____

_____

_____

_____

4. What is the command of God's Word to you in Galatians 5:1?

_____

_____

_____

5. What did God do for you in Psalm 107:13–22?

_____

_____

_____

6. In Psalm 107:13–22, what should you do in response?

_____

_____

_____

KNOW WHO YOU ARE IN CHRIST

When you renew your mind (Romans 12:2) to be transformed by God's Word, it is manifested by your daily actions. Put off the old mind that you are just a sinner and put on the new mind that you are a holy saint. When you believe you are *"just a sinner,"* you will act like a sinner. When your mind agrees with who you are in Christ, you no longer are complacent in sin, but live to imitate Christ.

Know your identity in Christ—you are dead to sin and its strongholds (Romans 6). Believe the Word of God! You must transform your life, thoughts, conversations, actions, and attitudes to the Word of God.

1. According to Revelation 12:11, what does God's Word say about you?

   _____

   _____

   _____

2. In what specific area of your life can you apply this truth of God's Word?

   _____

   _____

   _____

3. What does God's Word say about you in Colossians 1:13?

   _____

   _____

   _____

4. In what specific area of your life can you apply this truth of God's Word?

   _____

   _____

   _____

5. In Colossians 1:14, what does God's Word say about you?

_____

_____

_____

6. In what specific area of your life can you apply this truth of God's Word?

_____

_____

_____

7. In Romans 6:11–16, what does God's Word say about you?

_____

_____

_____

8. In what specific area of your life can you apply this truth of God's Word?

_____

_____

_____

OBEDIENCE—GO AND SIN NO MORE

Nowhere in the Bible does God command or permit the Christian to live in sin and be content. Contrary to popular belief, you cannot be a Christian and live any kind of way. God has standards for those who claim the name of Jesus as Lord and Savior. Throughout God's Word, He is exhorting you to turn from sin. You will not find in God's Word where He exhorts you to remain living as you did before accepting His Son, Jesus, to cleanse you from sin. If you are struggling with sin, the solution for being an overcomer is to abide in the Word. Transform your life to know you are dead to sin according to the sixth chapter of Romans.

 *Abide in the Word*

1. Write out John 8:11.

   _____

   _____

2. Write out John 5:14.

   _____

   _____

3. Write out 1 Corinthians 15:34.

   _____

   _____

   _____

4. What is God's command to you in the three Scriptures listed above?

    _____

    _____

    _____

5. List any sin(s) you may have that you have become complacent with or you justify as *"a little sin"* that God is *okay* with. Perhaps, your sin may be:

    ❣ Depriving your husband of sexual pleasure, whether you do so because of emotional disharmony, you are *just too tired,* or you are satisfying your sexual needs through masturbation of self without your spouse present (1 Corinthians 7:5).

    ❣ Faking orgasms or lying about sexual pleasure (Proverbs 12:22(a)).

    ❣ Having a grudge or anger toward your husband (Ephesians 4:29, 31–32).

    ❣ Being too stubborn or prideful in seeking restoration in your marriage (1 Peter 3:8).

    ❣ Doing evil for evil or "tit for tat" (1 Peter 3:9; Romans 13:10; 1 Corinthians 13:5).

    List your sin(s):

    _____

    _____

    _____

6. Study, memorize, and write out 1 John 2:6.

_____

_____

7. What sin did Jesus walk in?

_____

_____

_____

If Jesus did not walk in sin, neither should you!

- ♥ Confess your sins according to 1 John 1:9.
- ♥ Repent, and go and sin no more! (John 5:14; John 8:11.)

IT'S A SPIRITUAL BATTLE

Satan does not want you to overcome your sexual hindrances. Satan's job is to keep you in bondage, to believe you are supposed to sin, and to attack you every time you seek to be obedient to God's Word. God's Word says that Satan is a liar and he has been defeated. Yet, Satan continues to seek someone to devour. God has equipped you with a battle plan against the works of the enemy. Adopt the following battle plan for any sin struggle and sexual hindrance.

Take Every Thought Captive

Dwelling on the hindrance or problem gives Satan the ability to control your thoughts and your emotions. Ask God to release you from the pain of negative memory recall. "(For the weapons of our warfare are not carnal, but mighty through God to the pulling down of strong holds;) Casting down imaginations, and every high thing that exalteth itself against the knowledge of God, and bringing into captivity every thought to the obedience of Christ" (2 Corinthians 10:4–5 KJV).

Renew Your Mind

Memorize and quote the Word of God specifically pertaining to the struggles in your life. Do not allow the enemy to do battle in your mind (Romans 12:2; Colossians 3:2; Ephesians 4:22–24). "Whatever is true, whatever is honorable, whatever is right, whatever is pure, whatever is lovely, whatever is of good repute, if there is any excellence and if anything worthy of praise, dwell on these things" (Philippians 4:8). Be careful what you think, because your thoughts run your life (Proverbs 4:23).

God Commands You to Abide

*To remain
to reside
to stay
to continue
to remain till the end
to be steadfast
to endure
to be tenacious
to be persistent
to stand
to be immovable
IN HIS WORD
teachings
commands
sayings
John 15:4–7*

Keep the Door Closed

The enemy is sitting at the door of your heart and mind (Genesis 4:7). Do not open the door for Satan to return. Satan is seeking to devour you (1 Peter 5:8). He creates stumbling blocks and obstacles along your pathway to tempt you to fall back into sin or be hindered sexually (Matthew 16:23). Satan wants you to return to your old vomit (2 Peter 2:20–22). The devil wants you to get angry so he can have a foothold (Ephesians 4:26–27) and invite seven of his other demon friends into your life (Matthew 12:25).

You Are Equipped

God has already warned you in His Word that Satan is out to kill, steal, and destroy (John 10:10). He not only warned you, but God also equipped you for spiritual battle. Put on God's battle gear (Ephesians 6:10–18). Be ready at all times (1 Peter 4:7), and do not wait until you are on the battlefield; start training now for the devil's schemes, wiles, and trickery.

"His divine power has granted to us *everything* pertaining to life and godliness, *through the true knowledge of Him*" (2 Peter 1:3, emphasis added).

Stand Firm

Stand firm in your faith against the wiles of Satan (1 Peter 5:9; Ephesians 6:11, 13)! "Faith *comes* from hearing, and hearing by the word of Christ" (Romans 10:17). You hear the Word when you read and recite the Word audibly. Jesus resisted Satan by not only knowing the Word but also using it audibly as a weapon in spiritual battle against him (Matthew 4:1–3; Ephesians 6:17). When you are tempted to open the door to disharmony in the marriage or to sexual sin, speak God's Word against the temptation and flee.

Get Godly Counsel

Get biblically based counseling from committed Christian counselors who can counsel you in deliverance and freedom in the Word of God. You are strongly urged to seek counseling if you cannot seem to break free from your hindrance (strongholds). Wise counsel will direct you to be victorious over strongholds and the lies of the enemy through deliverance in Christ Jesus.

"The way of a fool is right in his own eyes, but a wise man is he who listens to counsel" (Proverbs 12:15). "In abundance of counselors there is victory" (Proverbs 11:14(b)).

Accountability and Spiritual Support

Get a trustworthy accountability/spiritual support partner (ASSP) who can hold you accountable to walk in your freedom in Christ. Refer to *"Accountability/Spiritual Support Partner (ASSP) Guidelines"* in Appendix B.

"Correct and rebuke your people when they need it, encourage them to do right, and all the time be feeding them patiently with God's Word" (2 Timothy 4:2(c) TLB).

 Prayer for Overcoming

Father God in Heaven,

I thank You for Your only begotten Son, Jesus Christ, who <u>has set</u> me free from _____ (specifically name the bondage, sin, or abuse). I thank You that because I am Your child, I have victory over <u>all</u> the works of the enemy (Luke 10:19). Father God, I choose not to allow Satan to kill, steal, and destroy what You have for me (John 10:10). I take back everything Satan has claimed, whether through willful sin, ancestral sin, or other open doors. I close the doors that may have been opened to Satan, and cover the door with the precious and powerful blood of Jesus Christ, my Lord and Savior.

I release all unforgiveness, bitterness (Hebrews 12:15), rage, animosity, and sinful anger (Colossians 3:8) I have toward _____, the perpetrator(s). I forgive _____ (name them) for their wrongs done to me and all that were a part of such evil (Acts 7:60). I pray for their salvation, that they will come to know Jesus Christ as their Lord and Savior.

Prayer for Overcoming

I confess the sin(s) of _____ *(name the sin(s)). I renounce the sin and every satanic stronghold. Forgive me and cleanse me from all unrighteousness. Cast my sin(s) as far as the east is from the west and remember them no more (Psalms 103:12). Thank You that I am not condemned, but I am forgiven (Psalm 32:1). Thank You that the blood of Jesus has made me as white as snow. Create within me a new, clean heart, filled with clean thoughts and right desires (Psalms 51:10–12). I receive Your healing from all wounds suffered as a result of these sins. I no longer walk in condemnation (Romans 8:1–3), but freedom in Christ Jesus. I will no longer allow sin to be master over me (Romans 6).*

*I choose to **Abide in the Word**, from this day forward. I claim the victory in Christ Jesus.*

In Jesus' Name I pray,
AMEN!

OVERCOMING FEAR

When there is fear in your life, you do not have confidence in God (Ephesians 3:12). God's Word says that faith comes by hearing His Word (Romans 10:17). If you are not hearing God's Word, you cannot abide in His Word. If you are not abiding in His Word, the spirit of fear can begin to rob you of being able to enjoy sex to the fullest extent. Some of the consequences of fear in sexual intimacy may be:

- Thinking your husband is sexually unsatisfied; therefore, he might choose infidelity.
- Comparing your husband to other premarital sex or fantasy relationships.
- Being seen naked.
- Getting pregnant.
- Verbalizing *sexcitement* to your husband or *"letting go"* during lovemaking.
- Looking *silly* during lovemaking.
- Giving of yourself, then your husband will want more and more from you, and he will not reciprocate (the one-sided relationship syndrome).

Christians have victory over *all* the works of the enemy (Luke 10:19). As a Christian, you must choose to stop allowing the enemy to kill, steal, and destroy (John 10:10) your sexual intimacy. You must agree and audibly quote the Word of God: "God hath not given us a spirit of fear; but of power, and of love, and of a sound mind" (2 Timothy 1:7 KJV). You are free, in Christ, to enjoy sex as God intended (Galatians 5:1). You must reclaim sex to be good, holy, pleasurable, and undefiled in the marriage bed (Hebrews 13:4).

1. Pray and ask God to reveal to you any and all fears you may have that hinder you from freely enjoying sexual intimacy.

2. How can you apply Luke 10:19 to be victorious over "all" the fears (works of the enemy) that you listed in No. 1 above?

_____

_____

_____

When you abide in the Word, you allow the seed of God's Word to be planted in your heart so you may produce a bountiful harvest of love, power, and a sound mind in your marriage.

 Prayer for Victory Over Fear

Father God in Heaven,

*I thank You for Your perfect love that casts out all fear (1 John 4:18). Forgive me for having fear and not abiding in Your Spirit of love (1 John 4:12–13). I will no longer live with a spirit of fear, but with Your spirit of power, love, and a sound mind (2 Timothy 1:7). I will draw near to You and resist Satan (James 4:7–8) when he attacks me with a spirit of fear. Thank You for giving me a spirit of power, love, and a sound mind. I choose this day to walk in Your victory and not fear. I now completely surrender (1 Peter 5:7) to You all fears, challenges, and inhibitions I have allowed to keep me in bondage from freely giving and receiving sexual pleasure and enjoying my marriage to the fullest. I will choose to allow Your Word to **ABIDE** within me because I am an overcomer in Christ Jesus (1 John 5:4–5).*

In Jesus' Name I pray,
Amen!

WHAT ABOUT STRESS?

Are you too stressed for sexual intimacy? The concerns of the world that affect your life can lead you to worry. Worry can cause you to experience stress. Stress can destroy your sexual intimacy as well as other aspects of your life, spiritually, physically, socially, and emotionally. Stress does not have any positive or Christ-like characteristics. It is imperative for you to take a closer look at any stress or worry you may have in your life.

CONTRIBUTORS

The stresses in life can come from many sources. Circle any of the following factors that are contributors of stress or worry for you.

Working Outside the Home

Stressed because of workload demands; work is unfulfilling, is time consuming (approximately ten hours of waking hours), and takes away from family time; work contributions may be unappreciated; you are dealing with the attitude and personality issues of co-workers, boss, customers; etc.

Performing Multiple Roles

Stressed because of trying to handle many tasks, yet perhaps not perfecting any, including: role of wife, keeper of the home, mother, caregiver, teacher, friend, church worker, employee, co-worker, daughter, sibling, extended family member, etc.

Being a People Pleaser

Trying to please people and make everyone happy, doing everything for everybody that asks of you, being unable to say "no" to requests to do for others, etc.

Façade

Giving the outward appearance that you are happy and everything is wonderful. Seeking to impress or keep up with *"the Joneses,"* with material goods, with image perception, etc.

Having Self-Imposed Perfectionistic Standards

Standards you feel others have of you: a spic-and-span house twenty-four hours a day, seven days a week; everything in its place; trying to have everything in control; you must be all and do all; you are trying to get everyone to live according to your perfectionistic standards; etc.

Self-Image Concerns

Overemphasis on outward beauty, you *must* have a "Barbie" doll figure; you are overly concerned about what others think of you; you want others to think highly of you; you must wear the latest fashion or purchase items from fashionable stores; etc.

Overwhelmed With Cares of this World

You are too caught up in the cares of this world and your "To Do" tasks, doing because you believe there is no one else that will do, being a caregiver to others, overwhelmed with the day to day matters of life, grieving from death of a loved one or some other tragic event, concerned with having financial security, performing household tasks and family tasks, etc.

Stress Factor of Parenting

What seems to be a never-ending cycle of parenting matters: beginning with the stage of new-born baby to infant, to toddler, to child, to pre-teen, to teen, to college years, to single years, to their marriage selection, and then to your grandchildren; parenting 24/7 responsibility; parenting multiple children and/or multiple births; disciplining conflicts; sibling rivalry; counselor; mediator; chauffeur; motivator; chef; maid; caregiver; concern for their safety and training, etc.

Stress Factor of Sexual Intimacy

You are overly concerned with your pleasure and your performance abilities; are fearful of getting pregnant, *again;* have a lack of knowledge or *"how to"* be sexually satisfying; are fearful of being seen nude; consider sex a chore or duty/obligatory responsibility; view sex as a waste of time; are too tired/fatigued; find it is not pleasurable or too messy; feel that your sexual drives are incompatible, etc.

1. List the reasons why you worry or stress.

_____

_____

_____

2. List the areas you feel you do not *really* worry or stress about, yet when you focus on these areas you may feel tense, frustrated, or overwhelmed.

_____

_____

_____

_____

3. Ask your husband, or another family member that intimately knows you, what he believes worries or stresses you. Be receptive to his input; do not be combative, defensive, argumentative, or feel you must justify your actions. List his responses here.

_____

_____

_____

THE CONSEQUENCES OF STRESS

When there is stress in your life, it can manifest in many ways. For example:

Spiritually

There is no peace because you are trusting in self, not God (Philippians 4:6–7, 9). Your life is chaotic because you have neglected God, who brings balance to your life when you place Him first (Matthew 6:33).

Emotionally

You become cranky, critical, angry, a nag, argumentative, resentful, and downcast, and display other ungodly traits. You become depressed (Proverbs 12:25).

Physically

You experience body aches, backaches, blood pressure elevation, and other ailments.

Socially

No one wants to be around you—not your husband, children, or pets.

Sexually

Often stress is negatively expressed toward your husband by neglecting or withholding sex from him, speaking negative words to him, or being curt.

1. List below the consequences of stress in your life. List how they affect you spiritually, physically, emotionally, socially, and sexually.

_____

_____

_____

2. With a gentle, calm, receptive spirit, meaning not confrontational or defensive, ask your husband to *describe you* when you are stressed. List his response.

_____

_____

_____

3. If your demeanor or interaction with others is not Christ-like, what can you do to make an *exchange* in your life? This means to put off (exchange) the ungodly traits and put on the new godly ways to walk in the manner Christ walked (1 John 2:5–6).

_____

_____

_____

VICTORY OVER STRESS

It is only when you abide in the Word that you can be victorious over stress factors in your life. Know what the Word of God says about stress and be a doer of His Word (James 1:22). You are hindered from s*experiencing sexplosions* when there is stress. If you are stressed, you must be the pilot of your life and Jesus the co-pilot. Change seats! The practical tips outlined in this section will aid you to be victorious over stress.

ASK GOD

You must address the root cause of your stress. The root cause is not fatigue. Fatigue is only the consequence or a fruit you are reaping as a result of some other seed that was sown. What have you sown in your life that would produce fatigue? If you fail to address the root of stress, you will always be picking at the fruit and never be an overcomer. You will continue to stress for the same reasons over and over again. What a vicious cycle! Get out of the stress whirlwind, and seek God's wisdom to determine the root cause for stress in your life.

If you are *not* spending time with God, you are probably not spending or even desiring to find time to spend with your husband. Look over your daily activities. If you have left out God and your spouse, more than likely you have stress in your life. Why? Because God is *the solution* to a stress-free life.

Pray and ask God to reveal the root cause of your stress. "But if any of you lacks wisdom, let him ask of God, who gives to all generously and without reproach, and it will be given to him" (James 1:5).

KNOW AND OBEY THE WORD OF GOD

If you abide in the Word, His Word is truth and the truth sets you free from stress. Here are the commands or teachings of God that you should know and obey regarding stress.

"Be anxious for nothing, but in everything by prayer and supplication with thanksgiving let your requests be made known to God. And the peace of God, which surpasses all comprehension, will guard your hearts and your minds in Christ Jesus" (Philippians 4:6–7).

"Casting all your anxiety on Him, because He cares for you" (1 Peter 5:7).

"Cast your burden upon the Lord and He will sustain you; He will never allow the righteous to be shaken" (Psalm 55:22).

HOPE IN GOD

In the midst of whatever you may be anxious about, give thanks (1 Thessalonians 5:18) and put your faith and trust in God. God has set you free from the chains and bondages of stress. "Why are you in despair, O my soul? And why have you become disturbed within me? Hope in God, for I shall yet praise Him, the help of my countenance and my God" (Psalm 42:11).

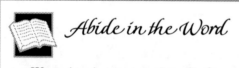

Abide in the Word

Worrying is not trusting God!
If you are not trusting God, then
whom are you trusting?
Psalm 56:3–4

To hope in God and put your trust in Him, you must abide in Him. Abiding in Him is evident by your faith and trust that whatsoever you ask, He will do (John 15:7). Do you trust God to handle life issues or do you trust yourself to handle them? Where is your faith, in God or yourself? Your hope has to be in Him and Him only for establishing and maintaining order in your life.

BE HARMONIOUS

Where there is disharmony in the marital relationship, there is always stress. If there are disharmony and stress, most often there is no sexual intimacy. Avoiding your husband, failing to spend quality relationship time with your husband, and putting other people or tasks before him open the door to a marriage on paper only. Be diligent in resolving relationship issues with your husband. Be obedient to God in establishing and maintaining a godly marriage. When there is ongoing marital conflict, it shows up in your marriage bed.

Abide in the Word

Read, study, memorize,
and daily quote:
Romans 12:18
Hebrews 12:14–16
1 Peter 3:8–13

MAKE LOVE

Do the one thing you need to do—have sex! God has uniquely knitted your body so that when you have an orgasm, your body goes into a relaxed state. Perhaps your husband falls asleep or goes into a relaxed state after he has climaxed. If you have never experienced a relaxed state of being after lovemaking, *Part III—Knowing* of this Workbook explains how to achieve multiple orgasms that will indeed alleviate the tension that stress produces.

During your menstrual cycle, are you stressed, cranky, crabby, and critical? When you are on your menstrual cycle, would your husband, children, and pet rather be on the rooftop than in the house with you (Proverbs 21:9)? God in His infinite wisdom designed sex not only for procreation, pleasure, and protection, but also as a stress reliever. A study conducted by reproductive researchers William H. Masters, M.D., and Virginia E. Johnson, former Research Director and Research Associate, respectively, with The Reproductive Biology Research Foundation in St. Louis, Missouri, found that sex at the beginning of the cycle relieved menstrual pain and discomforts. Additionally, having orgasms reduced pelvic cramping and backaches. You do not have to be stressed, cranky, and crabby during your cycle—make love to take the tension away. More information about Masters and Johnson and their research and making love during your menstrual cycle is in Chapter 9.

EXERCISE

There are numerous studies proving that participating in a relaxed, enjoyable exercise program can reduce stress and benefit sexual intimacy. These studies indicate that vigorous exercise, such as aerobics, may increase natural testosterone levels, strengthen the cardiovascular system, and improve circulation, which help pump blood to erogenous zones, increasing sexual sensation. Health professionals warn to avoid over training because it may produce fatigue and jeopardize the immune system.

> *Do not allow your concern about your outward beauty make you inwardly ugly*

To enhance your exercise program and increase the amount of time you spend with your family, make it a family affair. Doing so can energize and strengthen your relationships. Establish an exercise goal. But, beware! Do not allow your goal to produce added emotional stress on you and others. If your exercise goal is to lose weight, do not stress yourself and others when you may not be consistently making progress. Do not become stressed about losing weight. This is counterproductive. There are Christian-based ministries that can aid you in management of your weight. Refer to Appendix C for these resources.

If weight loss is not your goal, exercise anyway because regular workouts boost energy, improve confidence and your appearance, and give you a sense of well-being, according to numerous health reports.

RELAX

Being too busy can create unnecessary stress. Be aggressive to make a plan to set aside time so you can rest and relax.

Say "No."

Do you struggle with saying "no" to others when you know saying "yes" will cause stress on you? Be wise and do not allow your actions to cause stress on yourself. You cannot do everything for everybody. If you have difficulty saying "no" to others, stop and determine why. Failure to set boundaries with others may lead you to feel resentment, and unconsciously this resentment and all its ugly friends—bitterness, sinful anger, unforgiveness, and hurtful words—will show up in your marriage, including your marriage bed. Stop placing others ahead of God, your husband, and your family.

Eliminate, Delegate, or Regulate

You do not have to do everything in one day. Doing too much robs your husband of quality relationship time with you. You make yourself tired and stressed by having the expectation that:

- ❦ Everything has to be done before you go to bed.
- ❦ You must be at *this* meeting and *that* meeting and on *this* committee and *that* committee.
- ❦ You must do it or it will not get done.

- ❣ Kids have to be in almost all of the extracurricular activities offered.
- ❣ You need to be at the church nearly every time the doors open.
- ❣ You must host most of the social functions.

You must learn to eliminate, delegate, or regulate the tasks so you are not stressed.

1. List *all* the things you do, on a daily basis, that take you away from your home, such as meetings, church activities, children's extracurricular activities, work, errands, etc.

   _____

   _____

   _____

2. Of the tasks listed in No. 1 above, eliminate all that need to be eliminated. Ask your husband to help you identify what can be eliminated.

3. List all the *"gotta clean this"* or *"gotta do this"* tasks you can delegate to others, thus allowing you to have quality relationship time with God and with your husband.

Tasks to Delegate	I Will Delegate to
_____	_____
_____	_____
_____	_____
_____	_____
_____	_____

Relax your housekeeping standards

Learn to relax your perfectionistic housekeeping standards. Your husband and family will most likely be more responsive to work as a team to clean and maintain the home when you do not stress them to meet your perfectionistic standards. When the family works as a team with a pleasant *keeper of the home* (Titus 2:5 KJV), you will get more accomplished without stress.

Would your husband describe you as a meticulous, demanding, militant, perfectionist housekeeper?　　　　❑Yes　　❑No

Do you have to have everything done and everything in its place before you retire at night?　　　　❑Yes　　❑No

Do you stress yourself to have a *perfect and spotless* home at the expense of spending quality relationship time with God and your husband?　　　　❑Yes　　❑No

Do your high standards for perfection have a negative influence on others within your home?　　　　❑Yes　　❑No

Make and take a break

Your husband does not want to come home to a cranky, crabby, critical, stressed-out wife. Make yourself relax! Have some special escape time alone with your husband, at least twice a month. Escape time can include, but is not limited to, picnics, time at home without the children, inexpensive overnight escapes, walks in the park, etc.

Pray and ask God to help you relax and not stress about what else you could be doing. Do not feel guilty because you are taking a break. Establish time to sit and relax each day. Get a massage, take a quiet bubble-bath time, or just mentally relax. Learn to play and laugh with your husband.

Stop trying to be a SUPER WIFE

Your priority should be to become a godly wife. A godly wife does not stress because she is abiding in the Word. A godly wife does not stress, because her priorities are in order. A godly wife does not stress her husband and family to meet her perfectionistic expectations. A godly wife knows when to say "no" to the stresses of life. A godly wife knows that she must put God first, and everything else in life will be in order (Matthew 6:33). A godly wife is not stressed, cranky, crabby, critical, and complaining (Proverbs 19:13(b). A godly wife does her husband good all the days of her life (Proverbs 31:12).

Set Bedtime Standards

Free up quality quiet time for you and your husband by establishing and maintaining a designated early bedtime for your children. Be committed and consistent in putting them to bed at the designated time. You and your husband should identify a bedtime for all children to be in the bed. You should ask your husband to help you get the children ready for bed so you can spend quality, intimate evening hours together. Schedule this free time so that it can be used for bonding, reconnecting, spiritual growth, and/or sexual intimacy.

Participate in a Child Co-Op Program

If stress and time management are challenges for you, a Parent/Mom's Day Out may be an option you should use to your advantage. A Day Out is a church-based program designed for the purpose of allowing parents to take care of personal matters while their children are in a learning and playful church environment. Most programs are available approximately five hours a day, two days a week for infants and children up to five years of age. The other alternative to a church Day Out Program is to establish a similar program with other families. Your program can be rotated monthly amongst the other families.

A few of the stress reduction and time management benefits of using this type of program are:

- ♥ Accomplishing things you find difficult to do when the children are home.
- ♥ Completing, without interruption, some of your *"To Do"* tasks.
- ♥ Spending quality, intimate time with God.
- ♥ Spending quality, intimate time with your husband.
- ♥ Getting needed rest and relaxation.

When God reveals to you the root cause of your worry and stress, be diligent and obedient to give your burdens to the Lord. Cast the cares of this world on Christ. He neither wants you nor expects you to carry them (1 Peter 5:7). God's Word equips you with everything you need to deal with the cares of this world (2 Timothy 3:16–17). Applying God's wisdom is a practical means for eliminating stress. Choose to no longer allow the challenges of life to negatively impact your marriage bed through stress. You do not have to stress for any reason. Be victorious over stress through abiding in the Word.

NOT ENOUGH HOURS IN THE DAY

"Not enough hours in the day!" This adage has been around for a long time. Often it seems true that there are not enough hours to do all the things you want to do. Even if there were thirty-six hours in a day, it probably would not be enough for you. So, what is the real issue? Is it poor time management, or do you procrastinate from doing what matters most? Perhaps it is both!

There may be days when you have only two things you think you need to accomplish. Those two things should have taken you two hours to get done, but it seems as if you were just spinning your wheels and not going anywhere. At the end of the day, all you know is that you are tired, stressed, irritable, and frustrated, and cannot see where anything got accomplished. It is like a dog chasing his tail, going around and around in circles, never catching his tail. You are going around and around and never getting anything productive done. When you slow down from spinning around and around, you are too exhausted to do what matters most, which is spending quality, intimate time with God and your husband.

Whether you have one million things or just one thing to do, if you fail to spend quality, intimate time with God, you will always fall short of time. The solution is very simple: obey God's command to put Him first (Matthew 6:33) and submit your plans to Him (Proverbs 16:3). When God is first, everything else, including your time, falls into proper perspective.

When you fail to spend quality, intimate time with God, which is what matters most, you will search for more hours in the day and suffer from unnecessary stress, because you can't get all your *"To Do"* projects done. Where is your time going? Complete the following assignments to help you answer this question.

1. For this <u>current week,</u> list the top four things you have identified as priority on your *"To Do"* list:

    (1)_____

    (2)_____

(3)_____

(4)_____

2. For <u>last week</u>, list the top four things that were priority on your *"To Do"* list:

   (1)_____

   (2)_____

   (3)_____

   (4)_____

3. For <u>next week</u>, list the top four things you think will be priority on your *"To Do"* list:

   (1)_____

   (2)_____

   (3)_____

   (4)_____

4. Look at your schedule of daily events on a normal week. How much (give total hours) time was spent enhancing or investing in your relationship with:

   (a) God? My total hours of quality intimate time was: _____ (exclude church service).

   (b) Your Husband? My total hours of quality intimate time <u>alone</u> with him was: _____ (exclude sleep hours).

5. Consider your *"To Do"* lists. If Jesus had to prioritize them for you, how do you think *He* would arrange your list?

   (1)_____

   (2)_____

   (3)_____

   (4)_____

6. If you identified any modifications in question 5, why do you believe Jesus would make these changes?

   _____

   _____

   _____

7. How do you believe your husband would arrange your *"To Do"* list?

   _____

   _____

   _____

   Whether or not you know what your husband would modify, ask him to be sure. When you ask your husband what he desires of you, then faithfully and diligently do what he asks. Do not be argumentative or critical, or justify what you are currently doing. Your husband's recommendations could be how God has been trying to guide you.

8. Do you function according to God's family order—husband first, then children (Ephesians 5:21–6:1 and Titus 2:4)?
   ❏Yes   ❏No

9. Do you know you need to spend quality, intimate time with God, but it seems as though you just do not have enough hours in the day *to get to Him*? ❏Yes   ❏No

10. Do you know you need to spend quality, intimate time with your husband, but something always seems to come up that prevents you from giving him that time? ❏Yes   ❏No

11. Are you often too tired and exhausted to spend quality, intimate time with your husband? ❏Yes   ❏No

12. Does your job and/or your children take up so much of your time that it is too difficult to spend uninterrupted time alone with your husband? ❏Yes   ❏No

Review your responses to the above questions. If God is not priority in your life, the consequence is that everything else will be chaotic. If your life seems to be chaotic at times or all the time, check to see what matters most in your life. If you are saying that God matters most, yet your actions indicate He is not priority, it is time to accept reality and no longer make excuses for where your priorities lie. God has given you the solution in the commands of His Word.

Abide in the Word

1. Write out and memorize Matthew 6:33:

_____

_____

_____

God says you are successful only when He has been a part of the planning process (Proverbs 16:3). Put God first in your life's activities (Matthew 6:33). The following are some practical principles for establishing your priorities.

PROPER ORDER

God wants quality time with you, and not just at church on Sunday mornings or Wednesday nights. You will begin to transform your actions and thoughts to be obedient to all He commands in His Word when you place God first through spending quality, intimate time with Him. He commands you to have your priorities in order:

- ❣ God first (Matthew 6:33).
- ❣ Husband second (Titus 2:5).
- ❣ Children thereafter (Ephesians 5:21–6:1).

Quality time in your marital relationship becomes a challenge when the husband and wife have wrong priorities. If you have forsaken quality, intimate time with God, one of the many consequences is you begin to forsake quality, intimate time with your husband. Are you neglecting your husband because *you allow* other things—such as children, church, work, career, and "stuff"—to rob his time? God commands you to become one with your husband, not your children (Matthew 19:5). Do not place your children before your husband. Be obedient to God's divine order. BEWARE of your priorities!

MAKE TIME

Do not be just a hearer of these time management principles, but a doer! Develop and implement two **Action Plans**: (1) *"My Quality, Intimate Time With God"* and (2) *"Husband and Wife Quality,*

Intimate Time." Be aggressive and proactive in adhering to your Action Plans. Stop talking about what you need to do—just do it!

Spend quality, intimate time with God every day. Spend quality, intimate time with your husband every day. Schedule intimate time together in the same way you plan vacations, appointments with the doctor, going to church, other activities, etc.

Stop being B.U.S.Y. *(Burdened Under Satan's Yoke).* If you give Satan your time, he will take your marriage, too. What needs to be eliminated if your life is too busy? Readjust your schedule to include quality, intimate time with your spouse. Your plans do not have to be elaborate. Initially, keep the time simple and short. Time together does not have to always be sexual, although that can be rewarding. You can always make time for other unnecessary or unplanned activities—why not make time for God and your husband?

Do not wait for it to happen, but make it happen. Initiate! Do not procrastinate to make quality time with your husband. Be on guard for obstacles, hindrances, and the schemes of Satan that will get you off focus.

Eliminate time wasters: turn off the television, unplug the computer, and get off the telephone. Stay off the telephone! When your husband is home, stay off the telephone! Do not waste time chattering on the telephone when you can use that time

> ## *Make Time*
>
> *No time for each other outside of the bedroom can lead to several of the following sexual intimacy hindrances:*
>
> ❥ *Sex becomes a chore on the "To Do" list.*
> ❥ *Lack of desire due to no relationship outside of the bedroom.*
> ❥ *Strangers in bed ("two ships passing in the night").*
> ❥ *Unconscious or conscious resentment because the husband may take a break when he comes home from work, but the wife's work is never done and continues in the bedroom.*

with your husband. Make and maintain a time for all children to be in bed. When they are in bed, that time should be reserved for quality, intimate time between you and your husband.

JUST DO IT

Be creative to find time for sexual intimacy. How many opportunities do you let get away from you? Your life may be hectic, but that should not hinder you from being sexually intimate with your husband. Take advantage of the opportunities:

- ❦ If you are too exhausted at night, wake up early the next morning for an early morning love rendezvous.
- ❦ Take a shower or bath together.
- ❦ Make love during your lunch hour.
- ❦ Take a break from household chores and enjoy a love break.
- ❦ If you are a socialite, always visiting friends or relatives, go for a quickie in a private room of their home.
- ❦ *"Make out"* in the car. Car smooching and heavy petting is not just for teenagers.

You are now victorious over all that hinders you in being sexually intimate. *Sexpel* all your *sexcuses* and enjoy God's blessings of making love with your husband.

4

Emotional Intimacy

A marriage void of emotional intimacy will be void of *sex-plosive* intimacy.

EMOTIONAL INTIMACY

When spiritual intimacy is hindered in marriage, emotional intimacy is damaged. If emotional intimacy is damaged, sexual intimacy is impaired. Thus, every aspect of marriage needs to be in order: spiritual, emotional, social, and sexual. A break or crack in your spiritual foundation can be a detriment to your marriage.

If emotional intimacy goes unmet, frustration and detachment can occur in the marriage bed. This will be evident if you think your husband neither understands nor seeks to fulfill your emotional desires. If your husband is to live with you in an understanding way from an emotional perspective, it is imperative for you to communicate effectively and frequently to your husband about your emotional desires. In addition to communicating your desires, you must consider these important questions:

- Does he understand your meaning of emotional intimacy?
- Does he know how, when, where, and all other specifics to fulfilling your emotional desires?
- Does he know why you have these specific emotional desires?
- Does he know why you need to have these desires fulfilled?
- What would be your response if your husband chose not to fulfill one or all of your desires?
- Do you *really* need him to fulfill every one of your desires? If "no," which one(s) can you delete?

Someone once said, *"Understanding is the best thing in the world between a boy and a girl."* So, how would you and your husband grade the level of understanding between the two of you? One way to enhance your level of understanding of one another is to spend quality, intimate time with each other to:

- Know what *"emotional intimacy"* means for both of you.
- Develop an **Action Plan** for building and maintaining emotional intimacy.

❤ Identify what each of you desires emotionally.
❤ Communicate your expectations that perhaps have not been shared with each other since your pre-marriage dating days.

Address the following questions to help you understand *your* responsibility to build and maintain emotional intimacy.

1. What is your definition of *emotional intimacy?*

_____

_____

_____

2. What would you say is your husband's definition of *emotional intimacy?*

_____

_____

_____

3. Do you feel your husband fulfills your emotional desires? ❏Yes ❏No

4. If "No," how is your sexual intimacy affected when you feel you are not fulfilled emotionally?

_____

_____

_____

5. If you answered "No" to question 3 above, why do you believe he does not?

_____

_____

_____

_____

6. When was the last time you had an uninterrupted conversation with your husband regarding *when, where, how, why,* and the other dynamics about how he could specifically meet your emotional desires?

_____

_____

_____

_____

7. If you have not had this type of detailed, uninterrupted conversation with your husband in the last two months, explain why you believe your husband should remember or be *"all knowing"* about your intimacy desires.

_____

_____

_____

_____

8. Explain how family background, personality, and gender differences may play a role in the misunderstanding of and failing to fulfill each other's intimacy desires.

_____

_____

_____

9. What will *you* do to ensure that you and your husband understand and know how to fulfill each other's emotional desires?

_____

_____

_____

INTIMACY BREAKDOWN AND RESOLUTION

What happens when there is very little or no emotional intimacy in marriage? In most cases, every aspect of the relationship begins to break down. Look at the following outline to see how this occurs, why it occurs, and how to resolve this challenge.

HINDRANCE—Spouses Become Disconnected from Each Other

Why This Happens:

- ❣ You do not truly understand each other.
- ❣ You do not understand how to communicate with each other.
- ❣ You do not appreciate each other's differences.
- ❣ You do not know how to allow your differences to complement each other.
- ❣ You do not spend quality, intimate time together.

How This Happens:

Priorities change after marriage from:
- ❣ Dates to other duties.
- ❣ Flower money to diaper money.
- ❣ Husband focused to baby focused.
- ❣ Wife role focused to mother role focused.
- ❣ Free, relaxed time to responsibility chore time.
- ❣ Time with each other to time away from home or "To Do" tasks.

CONSEQUENCES of Being Emotionally Disconnected

- Lack of desire for sexual intimacy.
- Lack of effective, meaningful communication.
- Failure to appreciate the other's thoughts.
- Not completing one another.
- Others or "things" begin to replace the time you used to spend with each other.
- Heart becomes calloused toward each other.
- Compassion begins to dwindle.
- Complacency begins in the relationship.
- Temptation to engage in extra-marital affairs whether emotional and sexual, fantasy or real.
- Never cleaving.

COMMAND FOR RESOLUTION—Stay Connected to God to Get Connected to Your Spouse By

- Abiding in God's Word.
- Getting to the root of the emotional hindrance by identifying the what, when, where, and how you are emotionally disconnected.
- Acknowledging, confessing, repenting, forgiving, and correcting the hindrance.
- Understanding and appreciating him.
- Teaching, talking, and being transparent for him to *know* you.
- Discussing and implementing an **Action Plan** to get connected.
- Being considerate of him (Philippians 2:3–5).
- Changing the way you communicate. Change from ineffective to effective, which includes your attitude, your verbal and nonverbal body language, etc. (Ephesians 4:24; Colossians 3:5–14).

THE FRUITS OF OBEYING GOD'S COMMAND
(John 15:1–17):

When you and your husband are obedient to God, you will enjoy the fruit of intimacy by:

- ♥ Accepting one another—Romans 15:7.
- ♥ Being devoted toward one another—Romans 12:10.
- ♥ Building up one another—Ephesians 4:29.
- ♥ Glorifying God together—Romans 15:6.
- ♥ Honoring and preferring one another—Romans 12:10.
- ♥ Living in harmony with one another—Romans 12:16.
- ♥ Loving one another—John 13:35.
- ♥ Serving one another—John 13:14–35.

Abide in the Word

If you are disconnected and do not desire to be connected to your husband, you must understand the issue is about you and your commitment to Christ. You cannot say you are abiding in the Word and willfully choose to be rebellious to God's commands.
1 John 2:3–6

TIPS FOR CONNECTING

You must be aggressive to initiate a time for you and your husband to communicate with each other about building and maintaining emotional intimacy in the marriage. Do you find yourself asking, *"Why do I have to initiate?"* The answer is, "Why *not* you!" Who said *you* could not or should not initiate establishing and maintaining the emotional intimacy in your marriage? Perhaps your husband does not know you have a void or that you feel disconnected. This section gives you some practical tips for how *you* can initiate connecting emotionally, spiritually, socially, and sexually with one another.

HAVE THE RIGHT ATTITUDE

Exchange your old complacent, *"It's just going to be this way; things are not going to change"* attitude to agree with God's Word. Abide in the Word and know you will trust God to work all things for good in your marriage (Romans 8:28). When Satan gives you negative thoughts that your intimacy cannot be improved (James 4:7), speak to him as Jesus did, "Go, Satan!" (Matthew 4:10). Rebuke the enemy. Press toward the mark of renewal and reconnecting (Philippians 3:12–14). Let down your defensive guard; open yourself up to be best friends with your husband. (Proverbs 18:24). Be open to love and start anew in Christ (1 Corinthians 13:5).

BECOME ONE

Connect with your husband by being connected to God. You get connected to God through abiding in the Word. The Word of God commands the two of you to become one flesh (Matthew 19:5). Here are a few biblical principles for how the two of you can become one flesh:

✿ You must spend quality, intimate time with each other (that includes sexual and non-sexual time).

✿ Bond with each other by being of the same mind, maintaining the same love, united in spirit, intent on one purpose (Philippians 2:2).

✿ Get to *know* your husband: spiritually, emotionally, socially, sexually, and intellectually; his family background, etc. (1 Peter 3:7).

✿ Do him good all the days of his life (Proverbs 31:12).

✿ Do not drive him away by nagging or complaining, disrespecting him, and not honoring him (Proverbs 19:13; Proverbs 21:9, 19; Ephesians 5:33).

✿ Your body is his. His body is yours. Connect the bodies together to become one through the physical union of lovemaking (1 Corinthians 7:4).

THINK BACK TO WHEN YOU WERE DATING

Are you still inquisitive, not nosy, about his goals, desires, and interests? Become inquisitive again, with a new zeal. Are you still his cheerleader, his biggest fan, his encourager? Do you still give him interesting and exciting conversation? Or do you demand, *"Talk to me"*? Are you still caring and persuasive with your lips, eyes, and body? Are you eager to spend time with him in person and on the telephone? If you have allowed your *"new date zeal"* of the excitement and pleasure sensations to become stale, ask God to return these desires and actions and be creative to restore that zeal you had when you were dating.

YOU MUST DIE TO YOUR OLD SELFISH WAYS

Not everything is centered around you. Would your husband say *your* thoughts and actions are mostly *"Me, myself, and I"*?

(Philippians 2:2–4). Stop expecting him to be responsible for all the intimacy changes. Do you find yourself saying, *"Why don't you..."* or *"If you would only..."*? Expectations, especially non-communicated expectations, are sure to cause a disconnection in the marriage.

Stop trying to keep up with the *"Joneses."* Do not allow other men or marriages to be the standard for how you measure your marriage. The only standard you have is the Word of God. Make sure *you* are being obedient to apply His Word to *your* life. God said *you* can win *your* husband over by *your* gentle and quiet behavior, not by nagging him about what others are or are not doing (1 Peter 3:1–2). God blesses obedience (Deuteronomy 28:1–2). Win your husband over and receive blessings in your marriage.

Stop blaming him for everything that may be wrong or *"not the way they used to be."* God wants you to look at yourself in the mirror and address your faults (Matthew 7:2–5). If the flame has turned into a flicker, you can stoke the flicker until you build a hot, steamy, sizzling fire of passion.

Meet his desires the way he desires, not what *you* think is best for him or how *you* would want *your* desires met. You have to know what his desires are if you are going to meet them. You must ask him to know what they are. To ask him requires you to make time for him.

MAKE HIM A PRIORITY IN YOUR LIFE

You must aggressively make a choice to put him first over other things and people. You *can* find the time! There are no excuses for not doing so. You always seem to make time for the things that are important to you. How much time do you consistently make for God and your husband? Make sure your husband is second only to God. Your husband should not be at the bottom of your *"To Do"* list. He should not be after the kids, job, household tasks, friends, relatives, church functions, or hobbies. You must determine in your heart that you will spend time with each other. Reduce outside activities that take you away from spending time with him.

UNDERSTAND AND ACCEPT INTIMACY AND PERSONALITY DIFFERENCES

What are the characteristics of your husband's personality? Is he an introvert, conservative, reluctant to change, or sexually elusive person? If so, do not expect him overnight to become a James Bond or your Casanova. You may need to win him over gradually with gentleness and persuasiveness. You need to respond to your husband according to his personality, not yours. If you have difficulty knowing how to relate to your husband, attend a biblically based marital enrichment seminar that offers a topic on communication skills. The subject should include understanding one another's personality types or communication styles. Be committed to make your differences complement each other. Do not try to make him or expect him to be like you or some other man. Appreciate your husband the way God created him.

BE OBEDIENT TO GOD—JUST DO IT

Develop and maintain an *Intimacy* **Action Plan**. There are many good Christian resources that can give you pointers on how to reconnect as friends. But the best resource, which is often overlooked, is the Word of God. Abide in God's Word to help you develop and maintain an *Intimacy* Action Plan. "Knowing what is right to do and then not doing it is sin" (James 4:17 TLB).

Prayer for Restoration

Father God in Heaven,

I acknowledge and confess my sin of disobedience regarding intimacy with my husband (name your specific sins) (1 John 1:9). I acknowledge and confess my sin of withholding intimacy from my husband (1 Corinthians 7:1–5) and of being emotionally disconnected from my husband.

Father God, I confess I have had a very big log in my own eye and have been too busy looking at my husband's speck (Matthew 7:3–5). God, because of my wrongs, I have deprived myself and my husband of the blessing and joy of lovemaking as You intended. Father, I confess and repent of my sinful actions.

Help me to look at myself in Your mirror because I want to see myself the way You see me. I put away pride, selfishness, or old hurts that would hinder me from establishing and maintaining intimacy in my marriage (1 Peter 3:8–12).

I humbly submit myself to You for You to develop me to be the godly wife who freely gives of myself to my husband. Father, to do this, I make the choice right now to ABIDE in Your Word, so that I may be a doer and not just a hearer (James 1:22–23). Restore to me what I have allowed the locust to eat away (Joel 2:25).

In Jesus' Name I pray,
Amen!

5

No Desire, No Romance, and No Mood

*H*as the thrill gone? Is it not like it used to be? What happened to the desire, the romance, and the mood? Romance is the sparkle of *sexplosive* intimacy!

THE DESIRE IS GONE

It is imperative that you identify why you do not have the desire to be sexually intimate with your husband. Medical professionals, sex therapists, educators, and counselors all report many factors for lack of sexual desire. The lack of sexual desire could be one or a combination of factors such as medical, physical, spiritual, or social, or the marital relationship itself. You cannot s*explode* until you invest time into examining and resolving these factors.

SPIRITUAL FACTORS

Sexual Desire Robbers

Spiritual
Medical/Physical
Marital
Social/Psychological

They are out to kill, steal and destroy! Fear not! Jesus is your Healer! He came that you may have Abundant Life!

Ask God. Pray and fast, asking God to reveal to you the root cause for your lack of sexual desire for your husband. "Be anxious for nothing, but in everything by prayer and supplication with thanksgiving let your requests be made known to God" (Philippians 4:6).

When God reveals to you the root cause, seek His wisdom for how to address the cause so you may effectively apply His solution. "But if any of you lacks wisdom, let him *ask of God,* who gives to all men generously and without reproach, and it will be given to him." (James 1:5, emphasis added).

Do not allow the falsehoods of Satan to destroy your desire or attitude about sexual pleasure. Satan wants you to reject God's blessings of sexual intimacy. Abide in the Word to exchange your view of sexual intimacy to conform to God's view of sexual intimacy.

MEDICAL OR PHYSICAL FACTORS

There are many medical or physical factors that can negatively affect your sexual desire. That is one reason for women to have regular, complete health physicals. Select a physician who is not just a gynecologist, but who has extensive knowledge and experience in female sexual health. You must be willing to be transparent and share the specifics of what you experience or do not experience sexually. The following are things for you to consider that may be robbing you of full sexual enjoyment:

- Medications such as birth control pills, antihistamines, thyroid, diuretics, ulcer remedies, blood pressure drugs, antidepressants, etc.
- A change in your sexual desire after genital or pelvic area surgery (hysterectomy, tubal ligation, episiotomy, vaginal childbirth, etc.).
- Experiencing pain and discomfort during sex.
- Other health conditions that may affect your sexual desire: pregnancy; being postpartum; a hormonal imbalance; alcohol; diabetes; kidney conditions; decreased blood flow conditions (i.e., high blood pressure, heart disease, smoking); etc.

MARITAL RELATIONSHIP FACTORS

If you have become disconnected from your husband, you will not have the desire to make love to him. You may have a desire for sexual intimacy, yet that desire may not be for your husband. When you allow disharmony, whether by not initiating or by being stubborn to bring about a resolution, you open many doors for Satan. Unforgiveness, hidden bitterness, resentment, and anger are open doors for Satan (Ephesians 4:27) to kill, steal, and destroy sexual intimacy as well as every other aspect of your marriage. You must be diligent to resolve relationship issues with your husband.

Abide in the Word

You cannot have a bad relationship with your husband and a good relationship with God!

1 John 4:20–21

Regardless of who is at fault, you must seek to be at peace with him. "If possible, so far as it depends on you, be at peace with [your husband] all men" (Romans 12:18). If you have sinful anger and unforgiveness toward your husband or he toward you, go and be reconciled (Mark 11:25–26; Matthew 18:15)! If you and your husband seem unable to resolve the various challenges you may be encountering, seek biblically based marital counseling from a godly committed couple who has experience in marital counseling.

You may not feel physically attracted to your husband. Your lack of physical attraction toward your husband has a deeper root than his appearance. Godly love, which you should have for your husband, will transcend his physical appearance. If your husband has gained weight since you married him, you should be concerned about his health. If his weight gain is a "turn off" to you sexually, that is another perspective. If you are concerned for his health, you are concerned about his medical wellbeing. If you are turned off sexually, you are putting more emphasis on his outward appearance. God loves you just the way you are. Where you have imperfections, He washes and cleans you through His Word in love. He continues to provide for you. He continues to care for you. He still gives freely to you and does not withhold or deprive any good thing from you. How God loves you is the same way He wants you to demonstrate love toward your husband. God does not reject you, but loves you in spite of imperfections. God commands you to do the same toward your husband (John 15:12).

If you are turned off to the point that you have no sexual desire for him, you need to evaluate where the breakdown in the marriage is and begin to allow God's Word to abide in you. As God's Word abides in you, you will be transformed to have a godly love for your husband.

SOCIAL OR PSYCHOLOGICAL FACTORS

Many social or psychological factors may contribute to your lack of desire for sexual intimacy. There is ongoing research by medical, sexual, and psychological experts on how social and psychological factors impact sexual intimacy. Numerous sex and psychological experts have identified the following factors that can have an impact on your sexual desire:

- Stress and worry (depression).
- Major financial setbacks or work conditions.
- Traumatic sexual experiences.
- Lack of personal sexual satisfaction.
- Low or poor self-esteem or physical self-image.
- Priorities of life that are out of order.
- Negative teachings or no teaching regarding sex.

If these areas are not addressed, you will find yourself drawing further apart from your husband, emotionally as well as sexually.

OTHER FACTORS

As you begin to address why you may not have a desire for sex, some other thought-provoking questions to consider are:

- What barricades, whether mental, spiritual, or physical, have you consciously or unconsciously set up to block your desire for sex?
- Do you feel you lack sexual knowledge or skill?
- What is your level of satisfaction? If you are not satisfied, why not?
- If you used to have a desire, when did the desire begin to diminish, and what was happening in your life at the time the desire diminished?

It is through abiding in the Word that you are an overcomer. The answers to these challenges or sexual desire robbers have been addressed throughout this Workbook. You might consider seeking professional assistance to aid you in addressing any of the above factors that may be adversely affecting you. As you seek and apply God's wisdom through prayer, fasting, and obeying His Word, you will experience His victorious power, setting you free from all the factors destroying your desire for sexual intimacy. The key to freedom is abiding in the Word. God has an answer for every challenge you may face that would kill, steal, and destroy your sexual intimacy desire.

TO HAVE OR NOT HAVE SEX

SEXPLOSION QUIZ

When you do not have the desire, or your husband wants to be sexually intimate and you do not, what will you do?

A. Play sleep!

B. Remind him, *"We were intimate last week!"*

C. First, pray for God to change your attitude, heart, and mind to be in obedience to the Word of God. Then, surrender your body and mind to your husband and s*explode* in lovemaking.

D. Have sex grudgingly because you are physically and mentally disconnected.

Write Your Answer Here: _____
Correct answer at the conclusion of this section.

1. According to 1 Corinthians 7:5, what does "deprive" mean?

_____

_____

_____

_____

2. According to this New Testament teaching, for what purpose should you and your husband refrain from sexual intimacy?

_____

_____

_____

3. The Scripture states, "Except by agreement for a time." Why do you believe God needed to specifically set these guidelines for refraining from sexual intimacy?

_____

_____

_____

4. What are the consequences of depriving one another?

_____

_____

_____

5. How can Satan tempt the husband and wife if they deprive one another from sexual intimacy?

_____

_____

_____

6. If you are fasting and praying and your husband is not, what should you do if he wants to be sexually intimate with you?

_____

_____

_____

7. According to the New Testament teaching (1 Corinthians 7:5), does God say to deprive your husband because of your menstrual cycle, sickness, fatigue, not being in the mood, not looking pretty, depression, not feeling loved, fasting when your husband is not, or just not feeling like it tonight?   ❑Yes   ❑No

Abiding in the Word provides wisdom in knowing that sexual intimacy is for the protection of the marriage. When you abide in the Word, you cannot be selective toward which commands of God you will obey. You do not pick and choose whether today you will do what He commands and tomorrow you will not. When you deprive your husband, you are not only rejecting your husband but, more importantly, you are willfully choosing to disobey God. God has outlined in His Word why it is important to not deprive one another.

ANSWER TO SECTION QUIZ

The correct answer is "C." It is only through abiding in the Word that you can be obedient to God to sexually respond to your husband. When you are abiding in the Word, you understand that even though you do not initially _feel_ like being intimate, your follow-through to respond will reap blessings for both of you in the end. You do all things as unto the Lord, without grumbling or complaining and not grudgingly. (Philippians 2:14; 2 Corinthians 9:7.)

Prayer for Obedience

Father God in Heaven,

Thank You for caring so much for marriage that You instructed me to not withhold sexual pleasure from my husband, so we would not yield to the temptations of Satan (1 Corinthians 7:5).

God, I choose to respond to the desires of my husband, even when I do not feel like being sexual. I do so not under compulsion, but willingly, as You would have me (1 Peter 5:2(b)). In everything I do, I do it whole-heartedly. I will put my whole self into making love (Colossians 3:22–23). I will consider my husband's desires greater than my own (Philippians 2:3–4).

In Jesus' Name I pray,
Amen!

GETTING IN THE MOOD

When it is time for you to be sexually intimate with your husband, if you are not in the mood, you can find yourself wandering in *Never-Never Land* or thinking about the next thing on your *"To Do"* list. When you are not in the mood, your attitude can be *"Let's hurry up and get this over with"* or *"Are you finished yet?"* That is definitely not the frame of mind or attitude God intended for sexual pleasure. To *sexperience sexhilarating sexplosions* requires the right mood. So, what is mood? Mood is your attitude, your frame of mind, or your approach.

How do you get in the mood to have the frame of mind God intended? First things first. To avoid faking or pretending that you are in the mood, first identify what is the root cause for why you do not have the right attitude. Correct the root and then replant seed in the good fertile soil of your mind to produce a true sincere attitude for intimacy. This section provides some practical tips for getting in the mood.

ENJOY NON-SEXUAL TIME

Non-sexual time can build, maintain, and reinforce positive emotional relationship bonds outside of the bedroom. When there is no emotional intimacy outside of the bedroom, resentment can build because sex can be perceived as nothing more than an obligation, a chore, or *"doing your duty."* You must be aggressive to build or rebuild your emotional relationship, which can enhance your sexual desire.

Non-sexual time is effective only if your husband does not feel that most of the time you share together already is non-sexual time. He may not agree to spend time outside of the bedroom to enhance what goes on inside the bedroom if he feels that he has already been neglected or rejected sexually. Here are some tips for enjoying non-sexual time together:

🌹 First you must meet his desires before you can establish effective non-sexual time.

🌹 Be aggressive in finding ways to spend more time with each other throughout the day.

🌹 Learn how to enjoy each other through meaningful conversations, not about household responsibilities or problems with the children.

> *Improving your marital relationship will make your sexual intimacy more fulfilling.*

🌹 Turn the noisemakers off: TV, radio, computers, play station, etc. Spend time talking.

🌹 Touch more frequently. Wherever you are, give him a light stroke, a gentle pat, or a soft rub. Rub his back. If pressed for time, give a quick stress-relief massage. Touching does not have to lead to sex, but it can enhance it. Hold hands as you go places.

🌹 Open your eyes while kissing. Practice eye locking as you caress each other. The practice of eye contact is likely to generate greater feelings of closeness.

🌹 Shower each other with hugs and kisses throughout the day. Do not wait until you are in bed to catch up on caressing, hugging, and kissing. *You* should initiate giving hugs, kisses, caresses, and other forms of affection throughout the day. That is right: *you* initiate and give! Who said the husband had to be the one to *always* initiate? Where did that expectation come from?

🌹 Make a commitment for one full year to give your husband a card or a letter once a week expressing your appreciation and love.

🌹 Attend family, church, or business functions together. Spend time with each other at these functions. Do not allow him to be on one side of the room and you on the other side.

🌹 Become best friends—laugh and play together. Do not be so serious and sensitive.

❤ Do not be a cranky, nagging, complaining, critical wife. No one wants to be intimate with someone with such an ungodly demeanor. This type of demeanor only drives your husband to the rooftop. He would rather be anywhere but in the house with you—at his job, *hanging with the fellows,* the gym, etc. (Proverb 21:9).

You initiate this type of non-sexual intimacy. Do not have the expectation that your husband should initiate or do the same for you. If you desire non-sexual intimacy, give it and enjoy it without the attitude or expectation that he should reciprocate. Your husband may not *need* this time of non-sexual intimacy in the same way that you might *need* it. Throw away your selfish attitude of *you do for me and I will do for you.* Throw away your expectation that your husband is *supposed to* initiate intimacy and rebuild your desire.

GET RID OF OBSTACLES

Do away with anything that hinders you from desiring your husband: fantasizing about others, lusting after others, thinking about old boyfriends, having emotional affairs, etc. Discard pictures, memorabilia, letters, keepsakes, and other items that remind you of other relationships. Flee from anyone—whether coworkers, friends, or church members—that you fantasize about or who act inappropriately toward you. Do not be drawn away by your own lust (James 1:14).

YOU HAVE NOT BECAUSE YOU ASK NOT

Whatever you desire intimately, ask your husband to fulfill it. Be specific as to what you want when you ask him. Teach him to fulfill your specific desires. Stop expecting him to know *what* you want, *when* you want it, and *how* you want it. When he fulfills your desires, be grateful. Express your appreciation to him. Build him up so he desires to do it more often.

Your husband is not all knowing. He may not always remember your specific sexual intimacy details of what, when, where, how, etc. There is nothing wrong with telling him kindly (without nagging or belittling) over and over again what you desire. Stop making love once a week, expecting him to remember next week *what, when,* and *how* you wanted it last week.

DON'T BELIEVE THE MYTHS

- 🖤 *Husbands are supposed to be romantic.*
- 🖤 *Husbands are skilled in knowing what to do to enhance their wives' desires.*
- 🖤 *Romance always ends in sex.*
- 🖤 *Husbands are supposed to initiate.*

Do not be deceived. Guard your mind against what is depicted in movies, romance novels, soap operas, talk shows, and other media. If these myths control your sexual desire, destroy them! These things create expectations within you about lovemaking and what your husband should or should not be doing.

THE HUSBAND IS SUPPOSED TO SET THE MOOD

1. Why do you have the *expectation* that your husband is supposed to set the mood for you to be intimate?

   _____

   _____

   _____

2. Does your husband know you *expect* him to put *you* in the mood for intimacy? ❏Yes ❏No

3. If "No," why do you have expectations of your husband that he has no knowledge of?

_____

_____

_____

4. Explain how you have allowed your non-communicated expectation to affect your intimacy toward your husband.

_____

_____

_____

5. Look at setting the mood from your husband's perspective. If your husband is already in the mood, why does he need to set the mood for something that he is already in the mood for?

_____

_____

_____

6. Does your husband need to be put in the mood for intimacy? ❏Yes ❏No

7. If you have the *expectation* that your husband should set the mood for you to be intimate, here are some questions you must consider:

a. Does he know when you are not in the mood? ❏Yes ❏No

b. Does he know what you need to get in the mood? ❏Yes ❏No

c. Does he know how to get you in the mood? ❏Yes ❏No

d. Does what you need to get you in the mood change from one day to the next? ❏Yes ❏No

e. If he has attempted to get you in the mood in the past, is he always successful in getting you in the mood? ❏Yes ❏No

f. If "Yes" to "7e," did you express gratitude? ❏Yes ❏No

g. Did you verbalize to him how effective he was? ❏Yes ❏No

h. Did you tell him what he did was what you wanted him to do all the time? ❏Yes ❏No

i. Did you focus on what he did not do? ❏Yes ❏No

j. Did you take him for granted and not even acknowledge what he attempted to do? ❏Yes ❏No

k. Even if you verbalized to your husband that he needs to get you in the mood, do you believe he knows exactly how to get you in the mood every time? ❏Yes ❏No

YOU, JUST DO IT

If you were truthful with the above questions, you would agree that you should not *expect* your husband to put you in the mood for intimacy. Beware of how you may be allowing your non-communicated expectations to negatively affect your intimacy. The best resolution is for *you* to enhance *your* own mood (attitude or frame of mind) for intimacy! If *you* need romance, then *you* be the romantic! Your mood for intimacy should not be contingent on your husband setting the mood for you. If he does, be grateful and express your appreciation, both verbally and sexually!

MOOD ENHANCERS

The Brain

Rejuvenate your sex organ—the brain! Think on the pleasure of relaxing and intimately enjoying your husband. Mentally focus on the joy of lovemaking, not the *"To Do"* list. Sexy thoughts break into sexy actions. Think sexually!

Five Senses

God has designed you to have sensory awareness. Use what He has given you to enhance your lovemaking desire and mood. Ignite your sense of touch, smell, sight, sound, and taste in your romantic ambience. You cannot feel sexy dressed like Aunt Jemima and smelling like yesterday's fried chicken grease.

    ❦ *Sight*—Adorn yourself with intimate apparel that will make your husband stop and pay attention to you. A women adorned with hair rollers, matted house shoes, a fuzzy ankle-length robe, flannel pajamas, and baggy, torn underwear is not sexually enticing.

- 💗 *Sight*—Remove the laundry and old newspapers out of the lovemaking chambers. The sight of these only remind you of your *"To Do"* list.
- 💗 *Smell*—Replace the scent of fried grease or dirty diapers with your favorite candle aroma.
- 💗 *Smell*—Place his favorite perfume on *his* favorite part of *your* body.
- 💗 *Hearing*—Play some relaxing music.
- 💗 *Hearing*—Teach your children what *"do not disturb"* means. Arrange for your children to be in bed every night at a standard designated time. Train them to stay away from your bedroom when the door is closed. The noise of children can be a distraction.
- 💗 *Touch*—Smooth out the rough edges and calluses on your hands and feet. Make your touches soft and sensual.
- 💗 *Taste*—Enjoy a pleasant and clean taste in your mouth. Have fresh breath for sweet and tasty kisses.

Relax

You will find that as you become relaxed and confident in being sensual, your husband will not only enjoy making love, but you will also.

- 💗 Make time to relax in a long, hot shower or bath.
- 💗 Avoid drugs, alcohol, etc. that may negatively alter your emotions, diminish your physical desire, or dry your natural lubrications. Discuss the side effects of medications with your physician.
- 💗 Eliminate mental distractions and other stresses.
- 💗 Give yourself some quiet down time without the children before you go to bed.

Lovemaking Chambers

Design your own lovemaking chambers to be a *Garden of Eden*.
Strong's Hebrew Greek Concordance defines the Hebrew meaning
of Eden (e'dun) as a place of pleasure, delicate, delight. Your lovemaking chambers, the location where you make love, should be a
place of pleasure, delicate, delightful, provocative, and sensual.

Your bedroom should always be a honeymoon suite. Free it of
mood distracters—laundry, toys, bills, etc. Children, including babies,
do not belong in the marriage bed. The marriage bed is the lovemaking chamber of the husband and wife. Children should not be allowed
to invade this private territory for any reason. If you have been per-
mitting your children to sleep with you, stop this practice. Nothing or
no one should be a hindrance to opportunities for sexual intimacy.

Always be ready! Design a handy, always ready-to-go *"sexplosion basket"* to keep available. Your *sexplosion basket* should
include, but not be limited to candles, lotions, oils, towels, antibacterial handiwipes, tease ticklers (scarves, feathers, fur), drinks,
foods, music, pillows, special erotic objects or love toys, etc.
Having to stop and find these items can be a distraction.

Spice It Up

Intimacy can become monotonous when sex becomes predictable.
Break away from the same old routine. Add some spice or spon-
taneity in your sexual and emotional intimacy. Sexual intimacy
should be pleasurable; therefore, *you* have to *make* it pleasurable.

- ❦ Put laughter and play in your relationship. Get rid of the
  bored room. Add some fun and excitement to your intimacy.
- ❦ Plan an inexpensive weekend getaway so you can be free of
  chores and relaxed to enjoy intimate conversation, lovemaking, and love play.
- ❦ If you travel a lot or go to a lot of social functions, add spon-
  taneity and surprise to your intimacy. Make love or do heavy
  petting in the privacy of wherever you are.

💗 *Flirt!* Do you still remember how to flirt? Make sensual eye contact. Let your body speak the language of lovemaking. Give verbal sexual innuendoes, work every part of you to get you and your husband *sexcited:* intense stares, warm touches, raised eyebrows, and a gamut of facial expressions, and speak in a seductive voice tone.

> *You can enhance your sexual intimacy mood by becoming the aggressor in establishing a romantic physical and mental ambience*

Intentionally brush up against his body without breaking the contact. A well-placed touch at the proper time can communicate that you are giving him attention that you appreciate him or you "want" him. Be a tease and get him *sexcited* for what is yet to come. Use seductive gestures. Surely by now with those brief *sexplanations* you remember how to flirt!

💗 Behave like a teenager. Bring back the necking, kissing, petting, holding hands, and sitting up under or on top of each other. When you said, *"I Do,"* it was not supposed to put an end to the giggling, French kissing, necking, and smooching.

💗 Throughout the day, give him compliments and expressions of affection.

GO AND ENJOY

Now that you know *you* can take charge and be responsible for enhancing *your* own mood, enjoy making love to your husband to the fullest extent. Incorporate these and your own creative mood and romance enhancers every day, not just when you have *scheduled time* to make love.

Prayer for Attitude

Father God in Heaven,

I confess that there have been times when I knew my husband wanted to be intimate and because I was not in the mood, I pretended to be sleep or too busy. God, that was wrong of me. Please forgive me. I choose to never again withhold intimacy from my husband because I do not feel like it or I am not in the mood.

Father God, from this day forward I choose to have the right attitude or frame of mind regarding intimacy with my husband. I choose not to make love grudgingly, but with sexcitement. Help me to apply the intimate mood enhancers without expecting or demanding my husband to do them for me.

In Jesus' Name I pray,
Amen!

❧ *Part II* ❧

Serving

 Abide in the Word

"Give, and it will be given to you."
(Luke 6:38)

"It is more blessed to give than to receive."
(Acts 20:35)

"Do nothing from selfishness or empty conceit, but with humility of mind regard one another as more important than yourselves; do not merely look out for your own personal interests, but also for the interests of others. Have this attitude in yourselves which was also in Christ Jesus."
(Philippians 2:3–5)

6

Getting Him to Fulfill Your Desires

*D*o you want to have your husband running around asking *what he can do for you today*? Do you want to have him asking *how he can please and satisfy you*? According to John 15:7, "If you abide in Me, and My words abide in you, **ask** whatever you wish, and it will be done for you." You can get him to fulfill your desires through your abiding in three basic biblical principles of: **A**biding, **S**erving, and **K**nowing (**ASK**).

ARE YOU READY TO REAP?

Are you ready to reap bountiful fruit in your marriage? Are you ready to receive abundant blessings in your marriage bed? Are you ready to get your intimacy desires fulfilled? If yes, then you must apply God's principles to be able to receive. As you abide in God's Word, you will reap a harvest of blessings! Here is the principle of God's Word: to reap blessings, you must sow blessings. For getting your desires fulfilled, simply *A.S.K.!*

Abide in the Word!
Sow the seed of humble service!
Sow the seed of **K**nowledge!

ABIDE

The first practical biblical application of reaping is to abide in the Word. To reap you must sow the Word of God in your heart. It is only through abiding in the Word that you can continually give to your husband and not lose heart. If the Word of God abides within you, then your trust is in God to return blessings to you, not your husband. When you abide in the Word, you do not fall into a *"woe is me spirit,"* when it seems as if you are always giving and never receiving. When you abide in the Word, you remain steadfast on the reaping and sowing principles of God's Word.

Abide in the Word

1. Write out Luke 6:38:

_____

_____

2. Write out Acts 20:35:

_____

_____

_____

3. Write out a practical application for how you can abide in the Word of Luke 6:38 and Acts 20:35 and get your intimacy desires fulfilled.

_____

_____

_____

SERVE

The second practical biblical application of reaping is to serve. One true test of whether or not you are abiding in the Word is to serve your husband unselfishly by considering your husband's interests greater than your own (Philippians 2:3–5). You serve by freely giving to your husband. You serve your husband as Christ served you, unselfishly, without complaining, grumbling, or a negative attitude. Serving your husband communicates to him that you want the best for him, you want to please and satisfy him, and you want to be a godly wife.

Are you guilty of thinking, *"I already serve my husband. I serve my husband every day, when I cook for him, clean up the home, take care of the children, and so on and on!"* What you define as serving your husband may not be what he defines as serving him. If you have never asked him how you can serve him, all you are doing to serve him may not be what he desires. To serve him, you must know and do *what* he wants done, *how* he wants it done, and *when* he wants it done. Do not do what you think he wants or what you think he desires. That is serving and pleasing yourself, not him.

Serving your husband can either be easy or difficult, depending on the relationship you have with him. If it is a harmonious and equally yoked relationship, serving him should be easy. If you experience disharmony, a lack of spiritual unity and commitment, and a lack of communication, serving him may be difficult. If it is difficult for you to serve your husband, here is the solution:

 *Abide in the Word*

1. Write out Philippians 4:13:

    _____

    _____

    _____

2. Write out Mark 9:23:

    _____

    _____

    _____

3. When you do not want or do not *feel* like serving your husband, what assurance does God's Word in Philippians 4:13 and Mark 9:23 provide that enables you to serve?

    _____

    _____

    _____

4. How can you abide in the Word of Philippians 4:13 and Mark 9:23 and be diligent to humbly serve your husband?

_____

_____

_____

Serving your husband is trusting God to enable you to do what He wants you to do. To be obedient to God, you must have faith in Him to enable you to do the things your husband will ask of you. You cannot depend on yourself, because you will always give up, get frustrated, and slack

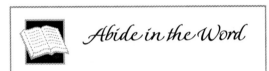

Abide in the Word

"Through love serve one another."
Galatians 5:13

off. But when you abide in the Word, you know that He has given you all you need to last, to remain, to be steadfast, to be determined, and to be a doer. He has given you power, faith, victory, longsuffering, joy, and peace to serve your husband. When things seem to be difficult for you, that is when you know you are operating in your own strength and power, which cannot compare to the wisdom and power of God. You *can* serve your husband, through Christ Jesus.

How do you practically serve your husband? Ask your husband how you can spiritually, sexually, socially, and emotionally serve him. Ask him! Do not assume you know what he is going to say. Ask your husband how he specifically wants you to serve him, including the details of *when, where,* and *how*. Take time to write out the specific details. Ask him to *teach* and *train* you how to serve him to *his* level of satisfaction, and not your level of satisfaction.

Here are important communication tips as you seek to sow blessings by serving your husband:

Be gentle and sincere in spirit when you express your desire to serve him. Your request to serve him may take him by surprise, so allow him time to think about your request. If he needs time to think, tell him to think about his answer, and he can share his answer with you tomorrow or a specific designated time. When you follow up with him at that designated time, approach him with a gentle, quiet, sincere spirit. If he does not have an answer, do not be offended or disgruntled that he has nothing to say. Again,

> *Giving and Receiving*
>
> *Only through abiding in the Word can you serve and give without the demand to receive in return.*
>
> *Acts 20:35(b)*

let him know you are sincere about serving him, and you may ask him at a later time or he can give you a response when he is ready.

When he makes his request known, do not be argumentative or justify your past actions. Avoid conflict or dissension. Receive his request with a cheerful heart and begin serving him.

KNOWING

The final practical biblical application of reaping is knowledge. Obtain and apply the knowledge of what, when, where, and how to serve and satisfy your husband. Knowing the right thing to do and not doing it only opens the door for disappointment. Your husband may feel, *"She knows what I like, yet she does not do it, so I will not do what she wants me to do."* That attitude prevents God's Word from being fruitful in both of your lives. If you have a negative and hurtful attitude, you will reap negative and hurtful actions.

When you are committed to be a faithful doer, your giving wins the heart of the receiver to want to reciprocate. So after you gain the knowledge of how you can serve your husband to fulfill his specific desires, apply the knowledge.

Be a doer. You must be faithful and committed to fulfilling *his* desires (Luke 6:31). Be consistent in serving him. Do not wait until you *feel* like it, because you might never *feel* like serving him. Do not be guilty of doing for him what you want done for you. What pleases you may not be what pleases him. Do as he asks, not as you desire. Guard your attitude. Your attitude and actions must *not* be hypocritical as you seek to serve him. Your husband must know you are sincere and that you want to please him. He must know you are not doing just to get in return.

 *Abide in the Word*

1. Write out the first part of Hosea 4:6(a):

_____

_____

_____

2. If you do not gain and apply the knowledge of *what, when, where,* and *how* to serve and satisfy your husband, how can your intimacy be affected negatively?

_____

_____

_____

If you want your husband to serve you, you must serve him. As you abide in the Word, rejoice in knowing that Jesus would not ask you to do the impossible. You have no greater example than Jesus. He was steadfast and remained focused on what He came to do (John 17:4, 21). Jesus, as our example, was obedient to God and humbly served us (Philippians 2:5–9). Jesus is your example, so walk as He walked (1 John 2:5–6).

WHAT ARE YOU SOWING?

❣ *Does it seem as if you are always sowing, but never reaping any good fruit?*

❣ *Are you feeling as though you are always giving, giving, and giving, yet never receiving from your husband?*

❣ *Do you feel that you are always making the sacrifice, yet not getting anything in return from him?*

❣ *Are you tired of doing, doing, doing, and never getting, getting, getting?*

❣ *Are you thinking, "Why can't my husband do something?"*

❣ *Are you thinking, "Why do I have to do everything?"*

If this seems to be your situation, God's Word will help you begin to experience a change for the better. God does not want you to be deceived. Although you may think you are not reaping, you are. You are reaping whatever you are sowing (Galatians 6:7–9). Whatever you are giving is what is being given back to you (Luke 6:38). Perhaps the root of the matter is *what* you are sowing and *how* you are giving. Consider the following to evaluate *what* and *how* you are sowing and giving in your marriage.

If you are abiding in the Word, your sowing and giving *attitude* will be:

❣ "How can I serve my husband today?" (Galatians 5:13.)

❣ "Although my husband is not responding to me now, I trust God that through my continual obedience to His Word, in having a gentle and quiet, serving spirit, my husband will be won over" (1 Peter 3:1).

❣ "I will faithfully demonstrate love to my husband without grumbling or complaining" (Philippians 2:14).

❣ "I will have the attitude of Christ: giving freely, serving sacrificially, and esteeming my husband's desires greater than my own" (Philippians 2:3–4).

If you are abiding in the Word, your sowing and giving *actions* will be:

- ❧ "Sow bountifully, for God loves a cheerful giver" (2 Corinthians 9:6–7).
- ❧ "Whatever you do in word or deed, do all in the name of the Lord Jesus, giving thanks through Him to God the Father" (Colossians 3:17).
- ❧ "Do your work heartily, as for the Lord rather than for men" (Colossians 3:23).

If you are *not* abiding in the Word, your sowing and giving *attitude* will be:

- ❧ "Why do I always have to…"
- ❧ "I am tired of doing all the time."
- ❧ "He never does for me, so I am not going to do for him!"

If you are *not* abiding in the Word, your sowing and giving *actions* will be:

- ❧ With selfish, wrong motives (James 3:14–15; Colossians 3:23).
- ❧ Doing so sparingly, grudgingly, or under compulsion (2 Corinthians 9:6–7).
- ❧ "With grumbling or disputing" (Philippians 2:14).

TIME FOR CHANGE

It is time for change if your sowing and giving reflect you are not abiding in the Vine (John 15:6). God's plan for change is pruning. You can no longer profess to be in the Vine and produce ungodly fruit. The fifteenth chapter of John clearly teaches that if you are not in the Vine and the Vine is not in you, you can do nothing. You cannot bear fruit of having your prayers answered, joy, a successful life, a happy marriage, peace, or victory.

You need to surrender yourself to God, the Vinedresser, for pruning (John 15:2). Pruning is painful and is not a pleasant process

(John 15:6). When you yield your life to God to be pruned, He cuts away your negative, critical, self-righteous attitudes and actions. He gathers up the dead branches of unforgiveness, bitterness, resentment, and the record of all the wrongs you have suffered and burns them. God cleans up your life so His Word can abide within you and you may abide in His Word. As you abide, the cares of this world and whatever your husband is not doing or should be doing will not choke out the godly fruit you sow. You will begin to sow godliness and reap godliness. The pruning process will result in a bountiful harvest of much fruit in your marriage (John 15:8).

ARE YOU ABIDING?

If you are not abiding, stop now and return to *"Abide in the Word"* and *"Meet the Lover"* in Chapter 1. Accept Jesus Christ, the Vine, into your life to be your solid foundation. To continue in this Workbook without abiding in Him will result in your trying to apply biblical principles with no foundation in Christ. Without Christ, the only true Vine, you can do nothing (John 15:4–5). If you attempt to apply the biblical principles in the Workbook without having a relationship with Christ, you will find yourself forever learning but never coming into the knowledge of truth (2 Timothy 3:7). You will always be trying, yet never succeeding in your marriage. You may receive temporary satisfaction, but you will not receive the lasting blessings of emotional fulfillment, joy, happiness, and peace in your marriage. These blessings come only when you abide in Him.

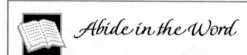

Abide in the Word

Want a harvest of bountiful blessings in your marriage?
*Then, you **must** abide in the Vine!*
John 15:4–7

YOU DON'T KNOW MY HUSBAND!

- ❤ *My husband is not going to go for these biblical sexplosion principles.*
- ❤ *He already thinks he is the king of sexplosions.*
- ❤ *It's not worth trying to get around his Casanova ego.*
- ❤ *He has a very sensitive ego. He becomes very defensive when I make recommendations. He says that I am trying to tell him what to do.*
- ❤ *He tells me he knows what he is doing and I don't have to tell him.*
- ❤ *He thinks only of himself; he is never considerate of my needs.*
- ❤ *I have told him before what I like, and I do not need to keep telling him.*
- ❤ *If he wanted to please me, he would remember what I told him and do it.*
- ❤ *He never does what I want him to do.*
- ❤ *He is too busy trying to get his needs met.*
- ❤ *I have been married too long to try to change now.*
- ❤ *You cannot teach and "old man" new tricks.*

1. How many of the above can you relate to your marriage?

    _____

2. If any of these are true for you, what impact does it have on the success of your applying the biblical *sexplosion* principles outlined in this Workbook?

    _____

    _____

    _____

3. In what ways do you allow your husband's actions or attitudes hinder you from being obedient to doing what God requires of you as a wife?

_____

_____

_____

4. According to your response to question No. 3 above, what can you do to stop allowing your husband's actions or attitudes hinder you from being obedient to God?

_____

_____

_____

5. What can you do to encourage your husband to respond to these biblical *sexplosion* principles?

_____

_____

_____

6. How can you change your attitude from the thoughts, listed in the beginning of this section, to conform to the Word of God regarding your husband?

_____

_____

_____

WHOM ARE YOU TRUSTING?

Change your attitude from *"You don't know my husband"* to *"I know a mighty God"*! If you truly know God, your faith and trust is in God, not your husband, for blessings. Do not allow the actions of your husband to dissuade you from believing that you can have a marriage according to God's design. God is far greater than your

> *If the Word of God abides within you, then your trust is in God, not your husband, to return blessings to you.*

husband is. Walk by faith that God will bless those who trust in Him, not by sight of what your husband is or is not doing (Hebrews 11:1). No longer allow your husband's actions to control whether or not you are obedient to do what God has told you to do to be a godly wife. Trust God, not your husband (Psalm 118:8) for blessings. "God blesses those who obey him" (Proverbs 16:20 TLB).

WHERE IS YOUR FOCUS?

Do you find yourself focusing on what your husband is or is not doing? Do you think about what you are always doing and he never does? Do you find yourself asking, *"Will this be the day my husband changes?"* Focusing on what your husband is not doing or should be doing hinders you from focusing on your total obedience to abide in the Word. You have lost focus when you begin to frequently think about *what* your husband is not doing, *when* is he going to become committed to Christ, *why* does he not respond to your desires, etc.

When your focus is on abiding in the Word, you trust God to fulfill all your needs (Philippians 4:19). Your focus should be on completely trusting God to bless you with joy, peace, fulfillment, and long-suffering while He is working all things together for your good in the life of your husband. As you abide in the Word, trust that God is watching over His Word to perform it (Isaiah 55:11). His Word says:

- 💗 Delight in God and He will give you the desires of your heart (Psalm 37:4).
- 💗 Have gentle, careful, and persuasive speech toward your husband. Being negative, critical, and moody will not get him to respond to you; it only turns him away (Proverbs 16:23).
- 💗 Renew your mind. Bury the negative past. Begin a new commitment to start fresh in building your intimacy. Do not allow old hurts, *what he will not do,* or *what he needs to do,* distract you from moving forward in enhancing your sexual intimacy (Romans 12:2).

Keep your faith in God, not in the day-to-day circumstances or what your husband is or is not doing. You will lose heart if your focus is on your husband. Whether your husband is or is not a Christian, your obedience to God does not change. Your actions and attitudes toward your husband must always reflect that you are abiding in the Word.

HARVEST TIME

If you are truly abiding in the Word, God is faithful to perform in your life what He has said. When you obey God, you will yield a bountiful harvest of blessings in your marriage. Keep trusting in God, not in your husband (Psalm 118:8). Be completely obedient to God—do not choose to obey only in some areas, but in every aspect of His Word (1 John 3:22). God does not lie; He will do what He says (Numbers 23:19; Jeremiah 1:12; Romans 4:21(b)). Remember, when you sow obedience, you reap blessings (Deuteronomy 28:2).

IF GOD SAID IT, HE WILL DO IT

You do not need to worry about *when* you will reap; just trust God that you will reap. Your faith must be completely in God for the harvest season. Prepare for the harvest by being obedient in service. God has said harvest time is going to come, so believe it will. What did God say?

- *If* you abide, ask and you will receive what you ask (John 15:7).
- Give and you shall receive (Luke 6:38).
- Sow, do not lose heart, and you will reap (Galatians 6:7–9).
- "*If* you will diligently obey the Lord, being careful to do all … all these blessings shall come upon you … *if* you will obey the Lord your God" (Deuteronomy 28:1–2).

IN EVERYTHING GIVE THANKS

When your blessings of harvest comes, follow the Word of God in reaping your blessings. Do not have the selfish demeanor of *"I have been so good, I deserve attention."* Do not have an arrogant attitude of *"It's about time!"* When you abide in the Word, your humble disposition is to:

- ❧ Be grateful. As your husband begins to give back to you, be grateful. Show appreciation. Do not be like the nine lepers who were so focused on themselves and what they received that they forgot to say "thanks" (Luke 17:11–19). Tell your husband "thanks!" Do not have a critical or complaining spirit if he does not meet your desires the way you would like to have them fulfilled. Give thanks to God for blessing you (1 Thessalonians 5:18).
- ❧ Be positive. Be positive even if what he did was not exactly what you desired. He did make an effort or attempt. Do not major on the minor things. Pray for the right opportunity to continue teaching him how to fulfill your desires.
- ❧ Be encouraging. Your positive response, verbal and non-verbal, can encourage him to serve you more. Encourage him to do it again, more frequently.
- ❧ Acknowledge him. Do not take the little things for granted. Verbally or in writing, acknowledge him for giving and serving.
- ❧ Serve him. Continue to serve your husband. Do not become slothful in doing good. Continue to give according to God's principles, and it shall be given unto you.

IF HE BECOMES SLOTHFUL

Have you ever been slothful in your obedience to God? Have you ever known what God would have you to do, yet chose not to do it? Have you ever started out energetically and enthusiastically serving in a ministry, then your desire and service drifted off?

If your answer is *"yes,"* why did you change? What was needed to keep you faithfully committed? Did God jerk your attention back to Him, or did He gently let you see that you had become slothful? Did God nag, complain, and ridicule you for losing heart in doing good? Did God say negative things toward you or hold a grudge against you for not being faithful?

In your slothfulness, God still loves you and is gracious toward you, and still meets your needs. God is very patient and kind toward you and that leads you to repentance (Romans 2:4). If your husband becomes slothful, your response toward your husband should be as God's response is toward you. God has "given you an example to follow: do as I have done to you" (John 13:15 TLB). Any behavior or

> *What is your focus?*
> *Serving or being served?*

attitude you have toward your husband that is contrary to what God does for you is a true indication that you are not abiding in the Word, but selfishly concerned only about *me, myself, and I.*

If you are focused on how your husband is not serving you, you cannot be focused on serving him. True and committed service to another means not keeping a record of what he is or is not doing for you in return. You should serve your husband as Christ served you. When your harvest time arrives, continue to abide in the Word and you will reap blessings as you sow them.

Prayer for Me, Myself, and I

Father God in Heaven,

Help me to die to self. Forgive me for having a "woe is me," "what about me," or "he needs to do for me" attitude. Let my sincere heart's desire be to serve, to give freely, and to not dwell on how much I do in spite of what my husband may not be doing. Let me give sacrificially as Jesus gave of Himself to me. I want to focus on giving and not receiving. I put off my selfish attitude and my nagging, grumbling, and complaining spirit. I receive Your servant spirit of "it is better to give than to receive."

In Jesus' Name I pray,
Amen!

7

Intimacy Talk With Your Husband

To experience a lifetime of *sexplosions*, there must be extensive, explicit expressions about sexual intimacy.

TELL HIM WHAT YOU WANT

How do you begin to talk with your husband about enhancing the intimacy in your marriage? If you are shy and reserved, you may be reluctant or timid to have a conversation with your husband about your intimacy desires. But be encouraged, "For God has not given us [you] a spirit of timidity, but of power and love and discipline" (2 Timothy 1:7, personalization added). On the other hand, if you are the type of person who gets straight to the point and has no inhibitions, it is important to approach your husband with a non-intimidating spirit.

Most often the husband and wife have opposite personalities. If

> *You must establish a sincere, committed relationship with God before you can establish a sincere, committed relationship with your husband.*

you are an introvert and feel uncomfortable talking about intimacy, perhaps he is an extrovert and is eager to talk. Your husband may be surprised to hear you initiate a conversation on intimacy, but he will more than likely be ecstatic and welcome the conversation. Understand that your personality differences complement each other. So do not succumb to timidity.

The answer to the question at the beginning of this section is that you must abide in the Word, and with a gentle and quiet spirit, through the wisdom of God's Word, develop and implement an **Action Plan** to talk about enhancing the intimacy in your marriage.

The remaining portion of this section will outline some practical guidelines for talking with your husband about enhancing your marriage.

WHY DO YOU NEED TO COMMUNICATE WITH YOUR HUSBAND?

As you plan to communicate with your husband, make sure you know *why* you want to talk with him. Some possible reasons are:

♥ To seek forgiveness for being disobedient to God in failing to maintain spiritual, emotional, social, and sexual intimacy in the marriage.

♥ To establish and implement **Action Plans** for how you can enhance your marriage to include spiritual, emotional, social, and sexual intimacy.

♥ To learn how to serve to satisfy him spiritually, emotionally, socially, and sexually.

1. List at least three reasons why you want to enhance your marital intimacy:

(1)_____

(2)_____

(3)_____

WHEN DO YOU SAY WHAT YOU NEED TO SAY?

There is an appointed time for everything (Ecclesiastes 3:1(a)). It is important to identify *when* is the right time to communicate with your husband. Before your first Intimacy Conference, you should consider the following:

♥ Address your sin issues with God first. Do not attempt to communicate with your husband until you have communicated with God. If you have sin issues in your life that you need to acknowledge, confess and repent of them. Establish a right relationship with God before you attempt to establish a right relationship with your husband.

♥ Spend time praying about *what* you want to communicate to your husband and *how* you will say what needs to be said (Proverbs 16:3).

❣ You must be committed to abide in the Word (John 15:1–17). If you are not committed to being obedient to God, all your efforts will be in vain. You will not reap a harvest of bountiful good fruit in your marriage.

❣ Talk with him when you have *his* undivided attention. Make sure he is not stressed or in a funk and that there is nothing that may interrupt the time, etc.

Intimacy Conference

This is a scheduled time for you and your husband to have a detailed conversation to establish intimacy goals to include the what, why, how, and other specifics for enhancing your marriage. Plan to have three Intimacy Conferences:

❣ *The _initial_ meeting to establish the intimacy goals.*

❣ *The _follow-up_ intimacy meeting to evaluate the progress in accomplishing the intimacy goals. Follow-up intimacy conferences can be monthly (every thirty days) until desired results become natural tendencies for each of you.*

❣ *The _final_ intimacy meeting to evaluate your successes in achieving your intimacy goals. Have a targeted date for consistently accomplishing your marital enrichment goals as outlined in your Action Plan.*

❣ Plan your conversation (Proverbs 16:3). Share your "mock" conversation with a godly husband/wife team, preferably someone who knows the two of you and whom you both trust immensely. Allow them to help you identify what would be good or not so good to say.

They may be able to help you prepare how to respond to your husband's objections or questions.

🖤 Schedule an Intimacy Conference. Set aside an appropriate amount of time with no scheduled obligations after the intimacy talk. Take the necessary steps to ensure there will be no interruptions or distractions.

Plan to have the Intimacy Conference when he has not been sexually deprived (or in a sexual drought phase) due to you sexually neglecting him. This is important, because if he has been sexually deprived, his main request or his focus may solely be on the frequency of sex. When he has not been sexually deprived, he will be able to give you meaningful conversation on intimacy that is not solely focused on the frequency of sex. As with all things, people tend to focus on what they do not have.

WHAT DO YOU NEED TO COMMUNICATE?

What you say should achieve the purpose you identified at the beginning of this section for why you want to enhance your marital intimacy. If you do not know what you are talking about, your husband will not know either. Based on your purpose or goal, consider the following for *what* you need to communicate:

🖤 Begin with prayer! Pray with your husband. Ask God to help the two of you communicate so each of you may understand the other. Ask for God's discernment, wisdom, understanding, peace, and harmony, and for His protection from Satan who seeks to kill, steal, and destroy this important Intimacy Conference.

🖤 If your husband believes you have wronged him by neglecting or depriving him of sexual intimacy, confess your sin to your husband, seek forgiveness, repent, and go and sin no more (John 5:14).

❣ Speak the truth in love. Unspoken things can fester inside and cause problems in the marriage. Determine if what you want to say needs to be said. If not, do not discuss matters that may cause unnecessary conflict or discord.

❣ Do not discuss prior relationships or experiences you may have had with others.

❣ Do not get hung up if you say something wrong. Stop and pray for God's help and guidance, and start over or move forward. Do not major on the minor things.

❣ Define the meaning of words used, such as "romance," "foreplay," "after play," or *"sexy."* Make sure the two of you understand one another and can explain the meaning of the words.

First, allow him to express his desires. Ask him to explain, in detail, what he specifically desires of *you* to satisfy and serve *him.* Make sure you understand what he asks or tells you. Ask him to explain *what, when, where,* and *how.* Write it down and read it back to him to ensure you have all the correct details.

Second, after you have identified what he desires, communicate to him what you desire. Be specific. Be clear about *what* you want, *when* you want it, *how* you want it, etc. You should write it down for him. Do not expect him to remember all you say.

Share with him how you desire to incorporate new lovemaking methods, positions, toys, and other enhancements. Tell him that you desire for the two of you to coach each other through all of the things outlined in this Workbook.Tell your husband you want him to teach you how to make love to him.

Together, develop and implement **Action Plans** for achieving goals to enhance your marital intimacy. Consider the following to discuss during your Intimacy Conference:

❣ How to arouse and sexually satisfy each other *every time.*

❣ How to please one another through kissing, licking, teasing, stroking, caressing, foreplay, and afterplay.

❣ What lovemaking methods, positions, and techniques you like or would like to try.

- What is a turnoff or brings frustration during love-making.
- What are each of your erogenous areas and how to best stimulate you to arousal.
- What sexy attire your husband wants you to wear.
- What part of your body he visually and sexually enjoys.
- Where your clitoris, clitoris hood, perineum, inner lips, and *U-Delight* are located.
- How to stimulate you to interval multiple orgasms.
- Whether or not you desire to have intercourse during your menstrual cycle.
- How to continue stimulating each other during climax.

If you need *love talk* throughout the day, make sure he understands what "love talk" is and what "throughout the day" means.

HOW DO YOU SAY WHAT YOU NEED TO SAY?

You must learn how to communicate effectively with your husband. You must understand his personality, his ego, and his style of communicating. Is he a planner or is he spontaneous; conservative or open-minded; extrovert or introvert; talkative or quiet? As you consider his personality, consider these tips for *how* to communicate with him:

- Ask God to teach you how to communicate with your husband. Apply the biblical communication principles in God's Word. The book of Proverbs is overflowing with biblical teaching on communication.
- Let your husband know if you are uncomfortable with having an intimacy talk, but to do so is important to the marriage. You both must be open and honest to express yourselves.
- Introduce your desire as a subject rather than a request or demand.

- Be sensitive to his ego. Encourage and exhort him. Do not be negative or condescending.
- Communicate positively. Say negative things positively. Learn to express your desires in a positive, encouraging, and motivating way. Death and life are in the power of the tongue (Proverbs 18:21)
- Communicate without blaming.

Put Off Negative Words

- *"There is no foreplay"*
- *"Don't be so rough"*
- *"You are cold and boring"*
- *"You don't ever kiss me"*
- *"You touch me only when you want sex"*

Put On Positive Words

- *"It really takes lovemaking to a deeper level for me when we kiss and stroke each other and take our time to make love slowly."*
- *"Once a week, let's try a new position or lovemaking technique, or make love in a different place."*
- *"Let's see how many times throughout the day we can touch and French kiss each other."*

- Do not complain, but compliment him.
- Stay focused. Do not get sidetracked on another subject or anything that does not accomplish the goals of the Intimacy Conference. Schedule another time to talk about issues that are secondary in nature or contrary to accomplishing the goal.
- Listen. Do not over talk your husband. Listen and understand! Do not interrupt.

❣ Do not make excuses for why you cannot meet his request. Do unto your husband as you would have him do unto you.

WHAT SHOULD YOU EXPECT?

If this is the first time you have aggressively taken the initiative to discuss intimacy, you should expect the unexpected. Plan for the expected and the unexpected.

❣ Expect God to work all things together for good (Romans 8:28).
❣ Expect God to do exceeding abundantly beyond all that you can ask or think, according to the power that works within you (Ephesians 3:20).
❣ If you are abiding in His Word, then you can expect God to answer your prayers regarding your marital intimacy (John 15:7).
❣ Expect God to bless your desires because of your obedience to continually show love toward your husband (1 Peter 3:9–12).
❣ Expect to reap what you sow (Galatians 6:7, 9).
❣ Expect a closer bond between you and your husband. Effective communication about sexual pleasure brings relationships closer. You become more intimate because you have become freer to discuss and share.
❣ Expect positive things to happen as a result of the two you developing and implementing Action Plans to enhance your intimacy (Proverbs 16:3).
❣ Expect your husband to be caught off guard by your request to serve him. He may not expect such a deep conversation from you, so give him time to think about his responses and to develop Action Plans.

- ❦ Expect your husband to be either honest and frank or reserved and suspicious. Do not become defensive or negative if you do not get an initial positive response.
- ❦ Expect Satan to attack. Satan's job is to seek to kill, steal, and destroy (John 10:10). Stand on the Word of God and the promise that when you submit yourself to God and resist the devil, the devil will flee from you (James 4:7). Follow Jesus' example of drawing near to God and resisting Satan (Matthew 4:1–11).

OVERCOMING OR DEALING WITH A NEGATIVE RESPONSE

Do not be deceived—Satan does not want Christians to enjoy God's blessing of intimacy, so he will put up every defense, roadblock, hindrance, and obstacle he can. Prepare yourself for spiritual warfare, *not against* your husband, but the evil one (Ephesians 6:10–18).

If the Intimacy Conference is not progressing, slow down or stop and pray. Seek God's wisdom about what the communication problem is and whether to proceed or reschedule the Intimacy Conference. If your husband does not want to lead in prayer, then you can either pray with him or by yourself, discreetly and silently. If the two of you have opposite communication and personality styles and intimacy desires, anticipate difficulties in the ability to be able to appreciate and comprehend one another. Be on guard—the devil is seeking to devour you, your husband, and your sexual relationship. Do not open the door for Satan to work through *you*. Your

Abide in the Word

"From a wise mouth comes careful and persuasive speech."
Proverbs 16:23 (TLB)

feelings or desires may not excite your husband, so do not be disappointed if he responds nonchalantly. Stay focused on achieving the goals for enhancing your intimacy.

Do not withdraw if you encounter what may seem like a brick wall, if you get your feelings hurt, if you are blamed for things, if he appears disinterested, etc. Continue to talk, gently and peacefully, to address the intimacy goals. Persuasively, with a gentle and humble spirit, exhort him to continue communicating. Do not be defensive if he gives negative or non-caring responses or demeanor. Do not return evil for evil, insult for insult, or *tit for tat* (1 Peter 3:9).

If he does not want to continue with the Intimacy Conference, do not lose heart and give up. Aggressively, with a gentle and quiet spirit, ask when can you reschedule another Intimacy Conference. Do not procrastinate in rescheduling the next Intimacy Conference. Do not walk in the flesh of bitterness, resentment, anger, and negative words. But walk in the Spirit by speaking in love and being kind and patient. You will win him over by your gentle and quiet spirit (1 Peter 3:1–3). You must continue to pray and fast for him and for your faithfulness to continue being intimate to him despite his actions. He may be skeptical of the "new you."

INTIMACY CONFERENCE CONCLUSION

At the end of your Intimacy Conference, recheck to make sure you have gathered all the specifics of the information shared. Make sure you have written out the specifics of each other's desires. You both must understand *who, what, when, where,* and *why* of achieving the intimacy enhancement goals you have established.

Conclude the Intimacy Conference on a very positive note. Express appreciation to your husband for participating. Let him know you are excited about serving him through fulfilling his requests. End with prayer. End with a kiss. Go ahead and give him a long, stimulating, erotic kiss. Maybe the kiss will not be the conclusion but the beginning of lovemaking.

You must trust God to be in control of changing you *and* your husband. You must ask God for His wisdom as you carry out your intimacy desires. Believe that God will answer your prayer as you abide in Him (John 15:7).

BE A DOER!

After you have concluded your Intimacy Conference, you must be a doer and not just a talker and hearer. This section provides some practical tips for how to implement the intimacy enhancement goals established as a result of your Intimacy Conference.

CONSISTENCY

Consistency and frequency are the keys! If you desire to see changes in you, your husband, and your marriage, then consistently and frequently achieve the intimacy enhancement goals. Be true to your commitment to change. Your change must come from your heart, not your head! If you slack off, he may slack off. If your husband senses you do not have a sincere heart, he may not commit himself to carry out the intimacy goals. Do

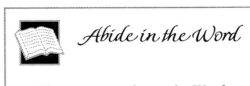

Abide in the Word

If you say you know the Word, but do not obey the Word, you are not abiding in Christ!
1 John 2:4

not change for one month and then go back to your old self. Move forward, not backward.

You must abide in the Word. If you stray from the Word of God, you will begin to do things in your own understanding, in your own ways, and for your own motives. There is no victory when you operate in yourself, only in Christ. You must seek Him first *and* His righteousness, and then all things will be added in your intimacy (Matthew 6:33).

FOLLOW THROUGH

Immediately begin to implement your Action Plans. There is no need to delay. Allow your Accountability/Spiritual Support Partner (ASSP) to hold you accountable to be consistent in fulfilling the requests of your husband. Not all your specific detailed issues on sexual intimacy matters can be presented to an ASSP; therefore, it is imperative for you to establish an effective system for how you can ensure you are meeting your husband's desires and achieving the intimacy goals.

Schedule a follow-up Intimacy Conference so the two of you can evaluate your progress in accomplishing the goals you outlined in the Action Plans that you developed. This follow-up Intimacy Conference evaluation should be thirty to forty-five days after the first meeting. You can make modifications in your goals, if necessary. Modifications should not be excuses for why you cannot make enhancements.

After the follow-up Intimacy Conference, schedule the final Intimacy Conference to make a final evaluation. The final date should be set for a time in which you can realistically achieve your marital intimacy goals. If you find major deficiencies, keep pressing forward to turn deficiencies into successes. Do not allow intimacy goals to fall by the wayside. Determine how you can improve, and do so.

MAKING IT ALL APPLICABLE

The following is an example of implementing an Action Plan. Do not take this example to be what your husband actually desires. You can meet his specific desires only by asking him what he specifically wants. This example serves to give you a practical application for implementing a request of the husband as a result of your Intimacy Conference. Again, the following example is only hypothetical, not actual.

Hypothetically, as a result of the Intimacy Conference, your husband's specific request is as follows:

HUSBAND'S INTIMACY ENHANCEMENT REQUEST:

"Increase the frequency of sex, and I want you to wear some of the sexy outfits I bought for you."

WIFE'S RESPONSE TO HUSBAND'S REQUEST:

First, you must get the specific facts. Do not assume you know what he is requesting. To be in one accord, obtain additional information regarding the specifics of his request. With a gentle, pleasant, and accommodating demeanor, obtain clarification similar to the following:

"When you say, 'Increase the frequency,' does that specifically mean every day of the week, or every other day, or Friday, Saturday, and Sunday, or exactly what?"
"When you say, 'Increase the frequency,' does that mean you want me to initiate all the time or more often? And, if more often, what does 'more often' mean to you?"
"When you say, 'Wear some of the sexy outfits,' are you specifically wanting more attire such as thongs, lace panties, net bodysuits, heels, crotchless panties, nippleless bras, a leather outfit, or what?"
*"When is it appropriate for me to wear my long flannel gown and other non-sexy pajamas? Do you **not** want me to wear my long flannel gowns and pajamas any more?"*

Second, to ensure you understand his specific requests, write out his request, read it back to him, or let him read it for accuracy. Then post it in a location where it will help you to remember what to do each day for him. A written example is in the "Just Do It" box in this section.

Third, after you have obtained all the facts, do not procrastinate. Be consistent in carrying out what he has requested. Do exactly what he has requested. Do not make your own personal enhancements without his approval. Your enhancements may not be what he wants. Remember you are doing what pleases him, not what you *think* pleases him. Put his desires before your own (Philippians 2:3–4).

"JUST DO IT" ACTION PLAN FOR SEXUALLY SERVING MY HUSBAND

The following is a practical, realistic, and hypothetical **Action Plan** for serving your husband. If your husband is not used to this type of royal treatment from you, he will be quite surprised and indeed satisfied. So, cut out this *"Action Plan for Sexually Serving My Husband"* and be a doer, not just a reader. *You* <u>initiate</u> the following:

<u>Sunday</u>: Give him an early morning, sunrise lovemaking service. Wake him up wearing his favorite sexy outfit. Give him a sunrise service he will remember throughout the day. If you are short on time, make it a quickie lovemaking rendezvous.

<u>Monday</u>: Put on his favorite perfume. Wear your new thong set or the set you forgot you had. Give manual stimulation to orgasm.

<u>Tuesday</u>: Arouse him by sight in the sexy outfit he bought you but you have never worn. Stimulate him with your hand but not to orgasm and conclude lovemaking in a position with a *rear view*. See Positional Illustration P–01 shown here.

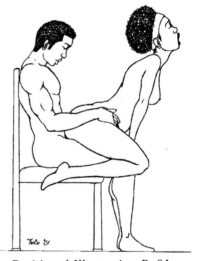

Positional Illustration P–01

<u>Wednesday</u>: Wear a sexy outfit that accentuates your husband's favorite body spot. Show off God's handiwork (your body) and be unashamed. Give him an on-top, backward astride position. Slowly pump your body up and down on his penis, so he can watch his penis go in and out of your vagina.

<u>Thursday</u>: Treat him as though he is your *lord* (1 Peter 3:6). Sit him in his *royal* chair. In your most provocative, erotic out-

fit, give him prolonged visual excitement. Excite him by teasing him visually. If he gets impatient, you might need help with your tie and tease love toys. As he is sitting in his royal chair, whether in bounds or not, throbbing with anticipation, slowly, teasingly, and provocatively make love to him orally. If he is in a reclining chair, recline him just enough for him to watch you make love to him orally.

Friday: Give him a reason to say *TGIF (Thank God It's Friday)*. Give him a special *happy hour* of pleasure. Enjoy him in a place or room where you have never made love. Give him complete sexual pleasure for an entire hour. Wear the negligee you may have outgrown *(he might like it tight!)*

Saturday: He needs a good, long workout. Dress up to slowly and sensually take it off, revealing a sexy outfit underneath. Give him a potpourri of lovemaking in various positions: Love him orally yet not to climax, then tease him with your hand yet not to climax, and then conclude with intercourse to *sexplode*. Surprise him with a new lovemaking position.

FULFILLED OR UNFULFILLED

Now that you have met his specific intimacy request (to increase frequency and dress more provocatively), ask him to evaluate your efforts. If his response is something like, *"Yes, you did far more above what I could ask or think,"* find out if he wants you to continue in the same manner or what modifications need to be made. If his response is *"No, you did not fulfill my request,"* ask him to tell you when, where, and how, and the specific details of how you failed. Do not lose heart in well doing; you will reap what you sow! Guard your mind against negative thoughts. Be careful: your thoughts will break out into actions (Proverbs 4:23). Just begin again to serve and fulfill him—which involve consistency and determination!

~ *Part III* ~

Knowing

As you have built upon the foundation of abiding in the Word, then serving to satisfy, now you can acquire the knowledge of physically *sexperiencing sexhilarating sexplosions* through:

- ♥ Knowing *how to* be a *sexpert;*
- ♥ Knowing the "key" to orgasms;
- ♥ Knowing *how to* teach your husband to bring you to multiple volcanic, orgasmic pleasure;
- ♥ Knowing *how to sexperience sexplosions* as God intended; and
- ♥ Knowing *how to* incorporate multiple love-making methods with specific techniques, positions, and other delights that will *sexcite* you and your husband.

8

Wonderfully Complex

Abide in the Word

"You made all the delicate, inner parts of my body, and knit them together in my mother's womb. Thank you for making me so ***wonderfully complex!*** It is amazing to think about. Your workmanship is marvelous—and how well I know it."
Psalm 139:13–14 (TLB) (emphasis added)

WITHOUT FLAW

God has made you without flaw! Yet, because of erroneous teachings or incorrect standards of society, many wives are ashamed of God's handiwork. If you are not abiding in the Word, you may be inhibited from freely giving your body to your husband unashamedly. Here is a brief listing of how your inhibitions may manifest in the marriage bed:

- Feeling that you have imperfections or flaws in your physical makeup that hinder you from being naked and unashamed.
- Thinking and feeling that your husband is not pleased or satisfied with your physical image.
- Lacking sexual confidence because you do not understand how God "knitted you together" to enjoy sexual pleasure.
- Lusting after the body of a TV model or other person.
- Having a poor self-image of your physical appearance.
- Depriving yourself and your husband of lovemaking pleasure because you are self-conscious about your physique.
- Failing to be visual *sexciting* to your husband.
- Being hindered in your mental lovemaking because your mental focus is on your physical appearance.

ABIDE IN THE WORD

How do you overcome these inhibitions? The only way to overcome these challenges is to abide in the Word. The Word of God is the only foundational truth that a godly wife should allow to control her attitude and actions. As you continue in this chapter, conform your life to the commands of God's Word. The following Scriptures declare how God fashioned you:

- ☙ "And God saw all that He had made, and behold, it was **very good**" (Genesis 1:31, emphasis added).
- ☙ "You are so beautiful, my love, in every part of you" (Song of Solomon 4:7 TLB).
- ☙ "For You *formed my inward parts;* You *wove* me in my mother's womb" (Psalm 139:13, emphasis added).
- ☙ "I will praise thee; for **I am fearfully and wonderfully made: marvellous** are thy works; and *that my soul knoweth right well"* (Psalm 139:14 KJV, emphasis added).
- ☙ "For **everything created by God is good,** and nothing is to be rejected" (1 Timothy 4:4, emphasis added).
- ☙ "And the man and his wife were both naked and were **not ashamed**" (Genesis 2:25, emphasis added).

AWESOME CREATOR

What an awesome God to take the time and effort to not just speak a word, as He did with His other creations, but to exquisitely mold, carefully shape, and completely design your body in His image. Every aspect of your being He touched. God knew just how He wanted you—how He wanted you to look and how He wanted you to sense the marvelous, sensational, *sexhilarating* lovemaking responses throughout your entire body.

EVERYTHING IS FOR ENJOYMENT

God does not declare any part of your body to be off limits to your husband. The book of Song of Solomon, in the Bible, is a detailed description of how a husband and wife made love to various parts of each other's body. Perhaps there are areas you need to incorporate into your lovemaking: your cheeks, your feet, your navel, your nose, and from your head to your toes. Yet many Christians believe certain body parts should be excluded from lovemaking. God's divine plan is for the husband to take the whole body of his wife as his own, and likewise the wife to take the whole body of her husband as her own (1 Corinthians 7:2–4). No part of your body is to be withheld.

Do not be disrespectful or ungrateful to the Creator for His perfect work in you. He desires that you glorify Him with your body (1 Corinthians 6:20). How do you glorify Him? By using what He has given you to satisfy your husband at all times (Proverbs 31:12) and enjoy the pleasure of sexual intimacy He designed for you. God has declared that everything is for enjoyment and nothing is to be rejected (1 Timothy 6:17(c)). Nothing is off limits to your husband for either sensory or physical sexual gratification.

1. What part of your body did God create that is disgusting, filthy, unacceptable, or to be rejected?

   _____

2. According to 1 Corinthians 7:4, what part of your body is off limits to your husband?

   _____

3. If the wife and husband are free in Christ to enjoy each other's full body, in what ways have you been depriving your husband of your full body?

   _____

   _____

   _____

   _____

4. What will you choose to do to stop depriving or restricting your husband of any part of your body?

_____

_____

_____

TIPS FOR BEING NAKED AND UNASHAMED

If your husband has not verbally said that you are sexually unattractive, then discard any negative feelings you may have about yourself. If you are just like you were on the day your husband said, *"I do,"* that is the way he likes you. Husbands view the physiques of their wives as beautiful, according to Bryan Bailey. He states, "Women are the only ones who notice their flaws, and if wives did not point them out to their husbands, husbands would not notice them." His profound perspective is that you should take heed to see yourself as your husband sees you.

If you have gained weight and it is affecting your health, you must not neglect addressing health concerns. There are Christian-based ministries that can provide assistance for weight management. Refer to Appendix C for these sources.

Abide in God's Word and conform your mind and attitude to believe nothing but what God says about you. You must abide in the Word to be set free from mental and/or physical strongholds that hinder you from accepting your body as being masterfully designed by God

> *How you feel about yourself relates to how you feel sexually.*

for sexual pleasure. Believe what God has said about you. Every day look at your naked body in the mirror and shout: *"I AM FEARFULLY AND WONDERFULLY MADE! THERE IS NO FLAW IN GOD'S WORK!"* Learn how your anatomy functions for sexual pleasure. As you begin to understand how God uniquely knitted your body together, you can praise Him for caring so much for you.

ALL THE DELICATE INNER PARTS

God has so wonderfully shaped your body that each part communicates with another part to lead you to *sexhilarating, sexciting sexplosions*. God connected not just the thighbone to the knee bone and the knee bone to the leg bone. But in His infinite Wisdom, He connected the brain cells to the nervous system and the nervous system to the blood system and the blood system to the skin, all to allow you to *sexperience sexhilarating* sexual responses. Consider all of your delicate inner parts. He knitted them together for you to *sexperience* sexual pleasure.

CARDIOVASCULAR SYSTEM

Includes the heart and blood vessels. During lovemaking, the heart muscles contract and the heartbeat increases, causing blood pressure to rise. As you stimulate an erogenous area, increased blood flows to the erogenous area, which enhances sexual arousal.

ENDOCRINE SYSTEM

Glands that secrete various hormones (testosterone, estrogen, and androgen) that influence your sexual drive. Consider doing additional research or study of the endocrine system to appreciate how God uniquely designed hormones.

MUSCULOSKELETAL SYSTEM

Tissues surrounding the genitals are highly sensitive. The PC or Pubococcygeus is the major pelvic muscle that supports the entire internal female reproductive organs and the anal area. This PC muscle is the same muscle that allows you to squeeze and release an object, such as a penis or tampon, that is inserted in the vagina. God also designed you to be very flexible and agile in your joints so you can maneuver your body into various lovemaking positions.

NERVOUS SYSTEM

Your body overflows with nerve endings. When you are stimulated or aroused, nerve impulses are triggered through the brain to the lower spinal column where nerve centers stimulate your vagina and other nerve-filled erogenous areas.

The Brain

It is a powerful sex organ. It controls your sexual desire, drive, thoughts, and moods. The cerebrum is the thinking part of the brain. Various lobes translate sensations, vision, emotions, and action. If you disconnect your brain from lovemaking, you disconnect yourself from all that God designed you to enjoy.

Firework Sparkle Imagery

"As Hollywood has often portrayed in movies, the culmination of a heated sexual experience is sparklers and bombs bursting in air. In many respects, they may not have been to far off," says Michael Burton, a leading doctor of optometry in Dallas, Texas. He reports, "This involves the process of synesthesia (sĭn˝ ĕs-thē´zĭ-ă). It is the concomitant sensation of a sense other than the one being stimulated, or the sensation in one part of the body or of an organ due to stimulation of another part."

"When a lady sometimes says, '*My man made me see stars,*' this is the experience of chromesthesia (krō´m-es-thē´ze-ah). Here, there is the perception of colors seen with certain sounds, smells, taste, phrases, or tactile sensation or stimulation," explains Dr. Burton.

How awesome! God has made you to enjoy fireworks as you *sexplode* in lovemaking.

When you are having an orgasm, the brain has other lobes that can affect your sound and feeling to experience crying or joyous laughter. Oh, what powerful *sexplosive sexperiences* God has designed within your body to enjoy during lovemaking.

Kissing

Sex therapists indicate kissing can send nerve signals from the tongue to the entire nervous system so that other nerve endings respond *sexciting* you sexually. Start kissing more often!

Five Senses

Enhance your lovemaking with tingling, intense, warm sensations. In the Bible, the Song of Solomon records many sensory stimuli in the joy of lovemaking. Identify how you can use all of your five senses to enhance your lovemaking. God incorporated sensitive areas or erogenous zones all over your entire body. These areas can be identified only when your husband uses all of his five senses to identify where your erogenous areas are located from your head to your toe.

GENITAL/REPRODUCTIVE SYSTEM

Be fruitful and multiply. The reproduction of godly offspring occurs in the reproduction system. The vagina connects with the penis during sexual intercourse to begin the reproduction process.

Ovaries

Two internal organs located on each side of the uterus. They produce the reproductive egg and sex hormones: estrogen, progesterone, and testosterone. These hormones are responsible for sexual desire.

Vulva Area

Includes the entire external genital area. Refer to Female External Genitalia Anatomy Illustration, *"Bed of Pleasure,"* of Chapter 8. The vulva area throughout this Workbook is referred to as your *bed of pleasure.*

RESPIRATORY SYSTEM

You pant with desire and your breathing rapidly increases during intimacy.

SKIN

The skin is supplied with nerve endings that are sensitive to touch, pain, heat, and cold, which provide the brain with information of where to rush blood.

> *Praise God*
>
> *There is no flaw in you.*
> *Song of Solomon 4:7*

BED OF PLEASURE

God skillfully designed the wife with a unique, intricate *bed of pleasure*—your genital area, which is your core area of sexual fulfillment. As you learn more about the intricate aspects of your *bed of pleasure,* you will begin to appreciate that God intended for you to enjoy sex. You will not be able to keep the good news of your uniquely designed *bed of pleasure* to yourself. It is imperative for you to share this knowledge with your husband. As he too becomes knowledgeable of how wonderfully made you are, he will begin to enjoy, appreciate, and comprehend the complexity of differences between the two of you. So learn, then go *show and tell* to your husband.

Allow your husband to visually *sexplore* your vaginal and anal love zones. To enjoy lovemaking to the fullest extent possible, you must allow your husband to appreciate your body by visually learning where your clitoris, clitoral hood, urethra, and inner lips are located. If he does not know where these key erogenous zones are located, you both can miss the dynamic *sexhilarating sexplosions* of making love.

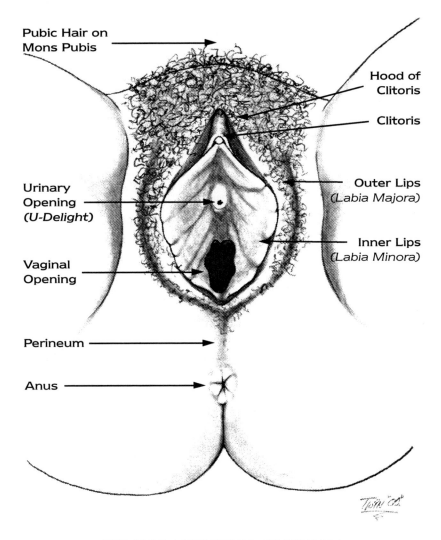

Pubic Hair on Mons Pubis

Hood of Clitoris

Clitoris

Urinary Opening (U-Delight)

Outer Lips (Labia Majora)

Inner Lips (Labia Minora)

Vaginal Opening

Perineum

Anus

FEMALE EXTERNAL GENITALIA
(Your Bed of Pleasure)
Anatomy Illustration

The resemblance of these external female genitalia may differ slightly than yours, but the parts are the same.

Anus

This is the opening beneath the perineum. The anus is where bowel waste is excreted. God filled your anus with many nerve endings like the clitoris. He situated your anus amongst all of your other genital pleasure zones. This is a sensual erogenous area that should be included in the lovemaking pleasure to enhance the level of sexual gratification.

Clitoris

Clitoris is a Greek word meaning "key." The *key* was uniquely designed by God for the sole *sexplosive* orgasmic pleasure of the wife. This small, pea size, highly sensitive, vital part has no other purpose than for your husband to give special lovemaking attention to it. The clitoris has a protective hood (upper fold of inner lips) covering because it is so sensitive. The clitoris is filled with nerve endings that give pleasurable sensations.

Outer Lips (Labia Majora)

The two major outer lips are covered with pubic hair. These outer lips and the crevices between the inner thighs are to be stimulated by your husband to give *sexciting* thrills to you.

Inner Lips (Labia Minora)

These are the two hairless lips inside the two outer lips. The two inner lips have an upper and lower section. The upper section covers the clitoris; the lower covers the urinary and vaginal opening area. This area is filled with blood vessels, and when caressed, teased, and stroked, the tingling sensation of pleasure can be *heavenly*.

Mons Pubis (Mons Veneris)

This is the mound of the vulva you see when a woman stands nude. It is covered by pubic hair. Allow your husband to *sexperiment* to identify what pleasurable sensations you can receive when this area is stimulated.

Perineum

This is the hairless outer area between the end of the vaginal opening and the anus. The perineum contains many sensory nerve endings and is *sextremely* electrifying when stimulated.

Urinary Opening

This is the urinary orifice located just beneath the clitoris and above the vaginal opening. Some wives experience sexual pleasure when the urethra (referred to in the Workbook as the *U-Delight*) is stimulated. The urethra leads to the bladder.

Vaginal Opening

This is the entrance into the vagina. The penis is inserted into this opening for sexual intercourse, which is the means for reproduction. The opening area is where the most blood vessels and sensory nerve endings are located. For location of the G-Spot, refer to Chapter 9.

Vulva

This is the proper name for the outer or exterior visible female genitals. The vulva area is often referred to as the vaginal area or *bed of pleasure* throughout this Workbook.

DISTINCTIVELY DIFFERENT

"In the image of God He created him; male and female He created them" (Genesis 1:27).

Do you sometimes think your husband *is* from Mars? Yes, the two of you are perhaps different in most ways, especially sexually. But the reality of it is, he is not from Mars. Consider your differences to be the way God designed each of you. God designed you to be distinctively different to complement each other, not to complain or be critical about one another. Consider some of your differences, and then learn how to appreciate and complement one another. The following are not standards but generalities of how *most* husbands and wives differ sexually. Consider the sexual intimacy differences between you and your husband.

HUSBAND	WIFE
Aroused Faster	Aroused Slower
Aroused by sight stimuli	Aroused by emotional and physical stimulation
Needs little or no pre-play	Needs pre-sex interaction (foreplay)
Orgasms quickly	Reaches orgasms slower
Orgasms usually once	Multi-orgasmic
Can separate sex and love	Prefers not to separate sex and love
Erotic sex talk appeals more	Appeals more to emotions
Can go more quickly from non-sex mood to sex mood	Goes slower from mood to mood
Needs less wooing	Needs more wooing
Usually needs refractory period between orgasms	Needs no break between orgasms
Usually enjoys less intimate positions	Usually enjoys more intimate positions
Desires to go from arousal to orgasm quickly	Desires prolonged lovemaking
Desires little or no post-sex interaction	Desires after love play interaction
Can be at odds with spouse and still enjoy sex (if proper stimulus is obtained)	Cannot be at odds with husband and enjoy making love.
Focuses on genitals	Focuses on whole bodies and feelings
Gets right to the physical pleasure	Heightens sensitivity by first creating the mood of romance
May want lovemaking tempo/rhythm fast and hard	May want lovemaking tempo/ rhythm slow

1. List additional sexual intimacy differences between you and your husband.

    _____

    _____

    _____

2. Explain how each difference affects your intimacy.

    _____

    _____

    _____

3. Develop and implement an **Action Plan**, contingent upon you alone, for how you will allow these differences to complement your sexual intimacy.

NO LONGER TWO, BUT ONE

To overcome these differences, you must abide in the Word to apply God's solution for the two of you becoming one (Matthew 19:6). When you abide in the Word, you do not dwell on *me, myself, and I,* or *what he ain't doing,* or *what he ought to be doing,* or *he got his satisfaction, but I didn't get mine.* You become one by making an exchange in your actions and attitudes to apply these biblical *be*coming one principles:

- ♥ Be in love with one another so much that your desire is to serve each other (1 John 4:7; Galatians 5:13–14).
- ♥ Be united in heart and mind with the purpose to fulfill one another (Colossians 3:14).

♥ Be mindful that your body is not yours, but belongs to your husband (1 Corinthians 7:1–5).

♥ Be considerate of your spouse's desires by learning about, understanding, and paying attention to each other (1 Peter 3:7).

♥ Be accepting of your differences as natural tendencies and do not assume that your husband is being inconsiderate of your desires (1 Corinthians 12:25; Romans 15:7).

God designed the two of you differently to complement each other. When you abide in God's perfect plan, His Word, you will complement each other. What a perfect plan! Apply His plan in your marriage bed and watch how your sexual differences begin to complement each other.

THE JOY OF *"TRADE OFF"*

If you and your husband are so distinctively different, how can you sexually enjoy your differences? Do you make your husband change to what is not naturally comfortable for him, or do you change to what is not naturally acceptable to you? Of course not! God has a better plan. His desire is for the two of you to get to know one another. When you get to know what pleases your husband and he learns what pleases you, you can *trade off* making love to each other. The *"Trade Off"* lovemaking method is the giving of sexual pleasure solely to either the husband or to the wife. It is an effective way to complement the natural sexual differences between the husband and wife. There may be times when your husband's desire is to focus solely on making love to you. In these instances, he gives you this *Trade Off* lovemaking royal treatment. He focuses on sexually satisfying and pleasing you in the way you desire to be pleasured.

BENEFITS OF TRADE OFF

Allows the recipient to:

- Receive sexual pleasure solely focused on her or him.
- Focus solely on the pleasure being received and not on giving pleasure.
- Relax and be pleased for as long as she or he likes.
- Accept love foreplay and afterplay, as desired.
- Not be concerned about her husband's quick ejaculation, which may be a natural tendency.
- Receive pleasure based on his or her own sexual desire or natural tendencies.
- Avoid the pressure of attempting to achieve simultaneous orgasms.
- Be sexually gratified if the giver cannot receive sex perhaps due to an illness.

Allows the giver to:

- ♥ Focus on giving rather than receiving pleasure.
- ♥ Seek to serve rather than be served.
- ♥ Learn and understand the physical pleasures of the other by studying, paying attention to, and being considerate of what the other desires.
- ♥ Give quality and quantity of lovemaking time to the recipient.
- ♥ Give the recipient what he or she specifically requests.
- ♥ Gratify the recipient if the giver cannot receive sex perhaps due to an illness.

In addition to the purpose of accommodating gender differences or just for the royal treatment, the *"Trade Off"* lovemaking method can be beneficial if one spouse is physically incapacitated and unable to receive sexual intimacy pleasure.

"Trade Off" is a signature of the Sexplosion In Marriage Series ™ of Abide In the Word.

Prayer of Thanksgiving and Praise

Father God in Heaven,

Hallelujah, God! I rejoice as I look at myself through Your eyes. I thank You for uniquely knitting me together in Your image (Psalm 139:13). Father God, You designed me without flaw (Song of Solomon 4:7). Thank You! Thank You for taking special time to design me with specific areas solely for the purpose of sexplosive orgasmic pleasure. Every part of my body is "very good" (Genesis 1:31; 1 Timothy 4:4). There is nothing "dirty," "shameful," "filthy," or "ugly" about my body. I will freely give my body to my husband for our pleasure (1 Corinthians 7:4). I will not be ashamed of making love to my husband, or of the wonderful, pleasurable, and awesome physical sensations You created me to sexperience.

I will boldly go and declare to my husband all the intricate parts You have designed within me for our pleasure. I can no longer expect him to know; I must show and tell him.

Thank You for designing my husband and me distinctively different, emotionally, sexually, and physically. I will no longer be critical of our differences, but I will learn how our differences can complement one another. I will be free to enjoy the "Trade Off" lovemaking method.

In Jesus' Name I pray,
Amen!

9

Sexplode

*T*he following sections are very *sexplicit* in providing specific sexual lovemaking knowledge, techniques, and illustrations. If you find any aspect to be offensive, you are encouraged to return to the beginning of this Workbook. Begin again by applying the Word of God to your life. Abide in the Word and you shall know the truth, and the truth shall set you free from that which hinders you from fully appreciating and enjoying all God intended for you sexually.

If you have omitted all the other sections of this Workbook and are starting here, **Stop! Go No Further!** You cannot address the physical aspect of sexual intimacy and overlook the spiritual and emotional components. You must first address the root causes of your inhibitions, fears, and marital relationship dilemmas. Do not pluck the fruit, meaning getting the sex technique information, if you do not have a solid biblical root in your life, thus in your marriage.

IS IT RIGHT OR IS IT WRONG?

Wrong views of sexual practices other than intercourse have held many people captive from enjoying a dynamic and fulfilling lovemaking *sexperience*. That is why it is imperative for you to abide in the Word, so you may know God's truth regarding His provisions for you and your husband to fully enjoy each other. God's Word should be your only standard for knowing He has placed no limitations on the parts of your body that are for *sexplosive* pleasure (1 Timothy 4:4).

Any *could nots, should nots,* or *would nots* you have must all be subjected to God's Word. God's Word is not silent regarding sex. Sexual intimacy is not a gray area in the Word of God. Abiding in the Word allows you to be strong and not weak in your faith (Romans 10:17), which will allow you to know there is nothing wrong, dirty, or unacceptable about what God has created for pleasure. Abiding in the Word sets you free (John 8:31–32) to enjoy your husband and allow your husband to enjoy you.

THE FINAL ANSWER

Is a sexual practice right or wrong? God has the final answer to this question. Unfortunately, many seek to find answers in everyone and everything else. Find your answers in God's Word. "Know what his Word says and means" (2 Timothy 2:15(c) TLB). God's answer, and not anyone else's, is the final answer. When you abide in the Word, you are able to stand on the truth (Titus 1:9). The Word of God is the only standard for determining what is right or wrong. Here are three key questions that can help in determining whether a sexual practice is right or wrong. First, is the practice condemned through the new and living way set up by Christ under New Testament teachings (Hebrews 10:19–24)? Secondly, does this sexual practice dishonor or defile the marriage bed (Hebrews 13:4)? Thirdly, is the sexual practice exclusively between you and your husband (Hebrews 13:4)? There are many sexual practices that could be considered, but the following are some common practices to put to the test.

FECES/URINE

The use of feces, bodily waste discharged through the anus, for sexual gratification is often known as "scat." The use of urine for sexual gratification is referred to as "watersports" or "golden showers." Medical experts state feces is bacterially defiled. The medical concern would be infection when bacteria are exposed to an open wound, abscess, or sore. Urine is not considered medically defiled. You must mutually agree this practice brings honor and respect to your marriage bed and toward one another.

A Biblical Test

❤ *Is the sex practice condemned through the new and living way set up by Christ (Hebrews 10:19–24; Hebrews 13:4)?*

❤ *Does the practice dishonor or defile the marriage bed (Hebrews 13:4)?*

❤ *Is the practice exclusively between the husband and wife (Hebrews 13:4 and 1 Corinthians 7:2)?*

FETISHES

A fixation or obsession with an object or body part where the real or fantasized presence is mentally necessary for sexual gratification. Sexual pleasure cannot be enjoyed unless the fetish is included. Lovemaking becomes dependent upon the fetish and not you or your husband. This is bondage that controls. The Christian should not be mastered by anything (1 Corinthians 6:12).

HYPOXYPHILLIA (CHOKING)

This is sexual arousal caused by oxygen deprivation through strangulation. Although this practice is exclusively between you and your husband, the greater concern is safety of the person being hypoxyphilliated or choked. There is a great risk of foul play if disharmony is in the relationship, the husband (or you) likes to demonstrate control or power in this manner, or the person being choked is unable to communicate some other emergency while being choked. This practice has the potential to create ill reversible harm, including death. This act could result in death and be classed as involuntary homicide, a crime. Murder is against God.

MASTURBATION

Masturbating yourself while your husband watches or participates can be voyeuristically *sexhilarating*. It is not marital oneness when a spouse has solo pleasure or masturbates while the other spouse is absent. Solo pleasure can be habit forming. No form of sexual intimacy should be done without the other. Choosing to masturbate absent of your husband deprives him of the pleasure of your body (1 Corinthians 7:3–4). Self-masturbation should occur only in the presence of the spouse if it *sexcites* the spouse.

THREESOMES, ORGIES, OTHER PERSONS OR ANIMALS

Hebrews 13:4 indicates that the marriage bed is not for adulterers and fornicators. Third parties in the marriage bed are unacceptable. Other persons (adulterers and fornicators) defile the marriage bed. Defilement may include, but are not limited to, orgies, threesomes, or ménage à trois; sexual acts with animals or other created beings; and sexual fantasies about someone other than your husband.

VIDEO TAPING AND PICTURES

Video taping and taking instant development-type pictures of each other can be risky. If you and your husband were simultaneously involved in an accident that incapacitates both of you, who could have access to this media? Such items do not maintain the privacy of the marriage bed. This type of media has the potential for someone else to view what should be between only you and your husband. Your body is for your husband, and your husband's body is for you (1 Corinthians 7:2, 4). Your bodies are not to be put on display for anyone else—that includes photo labs, video processing companies, or anyone that may unintentionally view what you may think is your own private media.

PORNOGRAPHY

Merriam-Webster's Online Collegiate Dictionary defines pornography as "the depiction of erotic behavior (and/or material) intended (the purpose, plan or goal) to cause sexual excitement." This behavior or material may include, but is not limited to, nudity events and places such as nude beaches, strip shows, sex educational videos; computers (internet); sex telephone services; and some movies, television/cable shows, etc. To translate this definition could be to say anything written or produced with the *intent* to get you sexually excited is pornography. God's *intent* for sexual intimacy is not for you to get excited by looking at someone else who is not your spouse. You are not to look with lust upon or fantasize about someone else (Job 31:1 TLB; Matthew 5:27–28).

Pornography dishonors the marriage bed because its *intent* is to get you sexually excited through creating an image of someone else in your mind, thus bringing a third party into the marriage bed. It takes the focus off each other and places it upon another. Something or someone other than your spouse is sexually exciting. You become sexually active with your spouse only as a means to fulfill your self-centered physical desire, but not to please and honor your spouse. Pornography is not exclusively between you and your husband because it always involves getting sexually excited by lusting, fantasying, or watching someone other than your spouse.

VIDEOS, EDUCATIONAL

Do "sex educational videos" dishonor or defile the marriage bed? Is this activity exclusively between you and your husband? Is this a mutual desire? What is your purpose or intent for watching? What is the purpose or intent of the producer? Will you become sexually excited looking at someone else? Will you begin to lust or fantasize about someone other than your spouse? Can you become addicted to or dependent on it for your sexual pleasure?

Whatever can draw you away from your spouse and feeds the lust within you to be drawn away to sin should be avoided (James 1:13–15). You should flee from anything or person that may cause you to sin or that can be habit forming (1 Corinthians 6:18; 1 Thessalonians 4:3–4). Your body is the only body that should be used to *sexcite* your husband. You are your husband's *sexpert*. You are the teacher; therefore, you educate him, not another women or couple on a video. If you are seeking "sparkle" and "something new," be creative with the mind God has given you and your husband to make up or create sparkle and add something new.

1. According to Hebrews 13:4 (NAS), what does "honor" mean?

_____

_____

_____

2. How does honor relate to the marriage bed?

_____

_____

_____

3. In Hebrews 13:4, what does "undefiled" mean?

_____

_____

_____

4. How do these things harm (defile) sexual intimacy in marriage?

_____

_____

_____

5. What other people or third parties have you invited into your marriage to defile your marriage bed?
   ❑ Another Person
   ❑ Cybersex (Internet pornography)
   ❑ Orgy or group sex
   ❑ Bestiality (Animals)
   ❑ Fantasy of Another Person
   ❑ Others: _____

6. Do you allow your children to sleep in your marriage bed with you and your husband?   ❑Yes   ❑No

7. If "yes," explain how your husband has said this has had an impact on your sexual intimacy.

_____

_____

_____

8. If your children are sleeping in your marriage bed, what will you do to stop your children from sleeping with you and your husband?

_____

_____

_____

If you question whether or not your sexual activity is right or wrong, put it to the test of God. Does Jesus Christ condemn the action? Does the sexual practice or activity involve or introduce others into your marriage bed, whether physically, emotionally, or mentally? Is it solely between you and your husband and no other created being? If you cannot pass God's test, seek to make an exchange to put off any wrongs, what displeases God, and put on the right things that honor God in your marriage bed. In addition to the various chapters within this Workbook, additional ministry resources to help put off any wrongs are listed in Appendix C. You may also refer to Chapter 2, *Hindrances to Sexual Intimacy,* and Chapter 3, *Overcoming Hindrances.*

BECOMING A SEXPERT

So you want to become a *sexpert*? Oh, you want your husband to become a *sexpert*? Becoming a *sexpert* is easier than you may realize. Here are some *sexpert* tips essential to *sexperiencing* a *sexplosion*. The two major components of becoming a s*expert* are teaching and *sexperimenting*.

TEACHING

Is your husband all knowing? Is he a mind reader? Does he know what you mean if you moan while making love? Does he know what you are communicating when you groan while making love? Does he know if you are in pain or in pleasure if you scream? If you say, *"Oh Yeah!"* does that mean, *"Oh yeah, hurry up and get this over with"* or does it mean, *"Oh, yeah, you are making me sexplode"*?

> *Talking is using words, not moans and groans.*

The key aspect of teaching is communication *(sexpression)*. You must talk with each other if you and your husband are to become *sexperts!* You must use words when talking, not moans and groans. You have been falsely communicating with your husband if you have been faking orgasms in the past. He may have believed your moans, groans, and screams were you *sexploding,* but truthfully you were not even close to an orgasm sparkle. Faking orgasms must be addressed. You will no longer need to fake orgasms once you begin to apply the *sexploding sexercises* within this Workbook. So, you must learn to *sexpress* your way to a *sexplosion.*

You are the key to your husband becoming your *sexpert*. Your husband does not know *what* you like, *how* you like it, *when* you like it, nor *where* you like it, unless you verbalize to him these important facts. He cannot read your mind, so do not expect him to know exactly when and how to apply the stimulation that takes you from one peak to the next. What you like today may not be what you like tomorrow. Your pleasure sensation could change from day to day, maybe because of emotions, physical conditions, or other reasons. Therefore, it is important that every time you make love, you always verbalize to your husband how to give you the ultimate stimulation pleasure. He knows what to do only when you use words to teach him what to do. Moans and groans do not tell him to stroke you here, to kiss you there, or to nibble you on your favorite hot spots. You must talk to him and tell him if you want stronger or gentler pressure. It is imperative for you to communicate to him the precise spot, the pressure, the rhythm, and all other techniques that give you *sexcitement*. Every time you make love, teach him.

There are many aspects of bringing a woman to *sexplosive* pleasure. Your husband may feel it takes so much to bring you to *sexplosion*. He may be overwhelmed if he tries to remember what you tell him from one lovemaking rendezvous to the next. Do not expect him to remember. Teach him before, during, and after how to make love to you. Do not assume he should remember what he did last time, especially if you are sexually active only once a month!

> *Women are more sexually complex and require more emotional and physical stimulation than men do.*

Another important reason for teaching your husband how to become your *sexpert* is what he may have learned prior to you may not be what *sexcites* you to *sexplosive* pleasure. Only you can teach him what *sexcites* you. Do away with the misconception that your husband is supposed to know how to please you. That misconception comes from movies, romance novels, magazines, soap operas, and many other tools that Satan can use.

Let him know the power and the pleasure of the orgasms you *sexperience*. Keep him *sexcited* about making love to you by building up his sexual self-esteem. Tell him how much you enjoyed him making love to you long after the lovemaking rendezvous. Send him a love note to tell him you are savoring the joy and pleasure of when the two of you made love. When your husband spends quality time sexually stimulating you, express your appreciation. Praise him before, during, and after lovemaking. When you are making love, praise and acknowledge how good he is, how well he is doing, and what he is doing to your body, your mind, and your inner parts. This will build up your husband's sexual self-esteem. *Sexalt* him by letting him know the quality and quantity of time he spends making love to you is worth it.

SEXPERIMENTING

How do you teach your husband what *sexcites* you to *sexplosive* pleasure? Teach him as the two of you *sexperiment* with the *sexceptional sexercises* listed throughout this Workbook. *Sexperimenting* will help you:

- 💘 Develop a better awareness of how you can achieve orgasms.
- 💘 Differentiate the levels of orgasmic sensations achieved using various methods of stimulation.
- 💘 Introduce new lovemaking methods, techniques, positions, toys, ideas, and concepts.
- 💘 Incorporate *sexcitement* and *sextraordinary* lovemaking activity.

Plan, Practice, Patience, and Play

The most important aspect of learning or applying anything different in lovemaking is *sexperimenting*. *Sexperimenting* requires planning, practicing, having patience, and keeping a playful attitude.

Planning means to think ahead to ensure everything is in place and is prepared for you and your husband to make love. If you do not plan, interruptions, distractions, and frustrations can negatively impact lovemaking. When *sexperimenting* with a new position, you may need to plan for proper props, consider body dynamics, gather what is needed to enhance the pleasure, etc. Plan to have all of the lovemaking resources, such as towels, oils, toys, and pillows, within arm's reach in your *sexplosion basket*.

Practice by *sexperimenting* can prevent frustration during love-making. Practice simulating new positions when you are fully clothed and not sexually aroused. Practice the stimulation of using a love toy before actual usage. The *sexcitement* of *sexperimenting* is practicing to turn bloopers into blessings.

Patience is required when you are learning something new or different. Trying something new does not mean you will get all the factors and details right the first time. It is important to understand to be patient with one another and with yourself. Turn *sexperimenting* practice sessions into playtime.

> *Sexperimenting is Sexciting!*

A playful attitude eases frustration and anxiety when things do not seem to go just right. Laughter makes the heart glad (Proverbs 17:22(a)). *Sexperimenting* should be fun and *sexciting*, not *sexhausting*.

Three-Strike Rule

Do not rule out any type of stimulation that could give you *sexplosive* orgasms until it has been tried and tested at least three times. Moods, atmosphere, setting, and other indirect factors may affect how you respond to lovemaking. You must be committed to planning, practicing, playing, and being patient when *sexperimenting* Try different methods, techniques, toys, or positions at least three times before you strike it out. Give it at least three attempts to master it or become a *sexpert*.

MENTAL SEXPLOSION

Sexperience sexplosions in your mind! You must be mentally attentive to *sexperience sexuberating* fireworks of *sexhilarating sexplosions* that bring tears to your eyes, spasms throughout your body, tingles in your feet, and throbs in your heart. Your sexual thoughts control your sexual responses and sexual actions. Allow your mind to indulge deeper and deeper into bodily *sexplosive* sensations. Allow your thoughts to mentally *sexperience* the pleasure your husband is giving you.

DISTRACTIONS

Many challenges can distract you from mentally focusing while making love. Mental distracters pull your mind away from the physical and emotional pleasure of sexual intimacy. You are distracted mentally if you are not allowing your mind to think about the physical sexual sensations you are receiving. You will not *sexperience* pleasure if you do not think about pleasure. Lovemaking begins in the brain. Proverbs 4:23 says your thoughts will break into action. During

Some factors that can negatively affect your marriage and will be a sexual distraction in the marriage bed are:

- ❤ *Communication problems*
- ❤ *Stress*
- ❤ *Anger, bitterness, and unforgiveness*
- ❤ *Disharmony or emotional strife*
- ❤ *Lack of trust*
- ❤ *Being unequally yoked spiritually*

lovemaking, are your thoughts about wanting to go to the next item on your *"To Do"* list, or are your thoughts about wanting to make love to your husband? You cannot *sexperience sexplosions* during lovemaking if your mind is in the kitchen or you are wishing your husband would hurry up and climax.

Children can be a distraction. You must teach your children that your lovemaking chambers are off limits. Teach them when and when not to enter your room. Set up appropriate standards and guidelines for your children to not interrupt.

You can be distracted spiritually if you are not abiding in the Word. The Word says to receive everything He created with gratitude (1 Timothy 4:4). You are not grateful if you are mentally rejecting sexual intimacy, which God designed. The Word says for you to have your own husband (1 Corinthians 7:3). You are not giving completely of yourself to your husband if you are mentally disconnected from him during lovemaking. The Word says to stop depriving your husband (1 Corinthians 7:5). Are you depriving your husband and yourself from fully *sexperiencing* the fulfillment of a *sexplosion* within you because you are mentally thinking about something else, thus hindering your physical pleasure?

HOW TO STAY FOCUSED

The following will help you *sexperience* deeper *sexplosions* by uniting your mind with your physical pleasure:

- 🌹 *Focus.* Focus on making love and not on chores, duties, responsibilities, and other distracters.
- 🌹 *Don't Worry.* Shift your attention from performance to pleasure. Stop worrying about your performance level. When you begin to worry about if you are doing *this* or *that* just right, you are focusing on performance, not pleasure.
- 🌹 *Let Go.* While you are making love is not the time for you to be *sophisticated.* You are too caught up in yourself if you are concentrating on keeping your composure because *nice girls* do not shout, scream, make sounds, or squirm in pleasure. Let go and enjoy what God has designed for your pleasure.

❦ *Talk!* Make provocative responses and verbally *sexpress* your gratification and pleasure. Your verbal *sexpression* of *sexcitement* can take your lovemaking to *sextreme, sexhilarating sexplosions!*

❦ *Think!* Allow your thoughts to enjoy what you see, hear, feel, smell, and taste. Indulge your thoughts to enjoy the warmth of your husband's mouth on your breast as he nibbles your nipples and kisses your areola. You can *sexperience* a deep level of mental and physical *sexplosion* as you are *sexcited* by your husband's every kiss, lick, and touch to every part of your body only when you mentally focus during lovemaking. If you are mentally making love, you can tell him where to put his mouth and how to kiss you, stroke you, and lick you at just the right moment. You can allow your mind to enjoy everything he is going to do to your body and your mind! Pay attention to your tingles, tickles, and tremors your body is feeling in your erogenous zones.

❦ *Be open.* You can enjoy him and he can enjoy you if your mind is open to the *sexplosions* that can come. Having a closed mind will cause you to miss the receiving and giving of all God has designed for you.

❦ *Enjoy.* Enjoy the bodily sensations and stimulations you are feeling.

You must identify what mentally distracts you during lovemaking and aggressively address those matters. No longer permit Satan to kill, steal, and destroy your mental focus during sexual intimacy. Take back your mind and begin to think sensually, provocatively, and erotically to enjoy all the pleasures God created for sexual intimacy. Mental attitude is the key to receiving multiple orgasms. You must be focused on lovemaking to achieve orgasms.

ORGASMIC SEXPLOSION!

Orgasms are most often described as a series of rhythmic contractions or quivers triggered throughout the body as a result of intense physical and psychological stimulation. Contractions are centered in the vagina, uterus, and the rectal sphincter, but may be experienced throughout the entire body for seconds. Once you identify and learn how your body needs stimulation, you may easily and quickly *sexperience* orgasms. It is important to remember that the sensation of an orgasm for a wife may be different every time.

> ### *Sexplosive Orgasms*
>
> *A sextraordinary, sexhilarating, volcanic, sexual climax experienced <u>only</u> when a husband and wife are connected through their thoughts, feelings, friendship, physical union, and commitment to Christ.*

THE BLESSINGS OF ORGASMS

Sex and medical experts report the facts of how God knitted your body together to benefit from orgasms. Many experts report the benefits of orgasms are:

- 💗 Condition the cardiovascular system.
- 💗 Impart a healthy glow to the skin.
- 💗 Improve overall body tone.
- 💗 Trigger the release of endorphins in the brain that can help relieve headaches, backaches, and other minor aches and pains.
- 💗 Relieve stress and tension (including premenstrual tension).
- 💗 Help you sleep more soundly.

HOW DO YOU SPELL RELIEF?

So you say you have a headache, backache, or PMS cramps hindering you from being sexually intimate with your husband? Well, God has a solution. No, it is not an over-the-counter tablet or prescription for analgesia. God's solution is all natural, has no side effects, and is free! Yes, it is O-R-G-A-S-M! If it is true when you say, *"Not tonight dear; I have a headache,"* then enjoy the pleasure of orgasmic *sexplosions* for relief.

Researchers are now reporting what God has told us from the beginning—sex, resulting in orgasmic release, is not only a stress buster but may ease pain as well. Ongoing research and studies are being conducted on the findings of sex as an analgesic. One leading researcher, Beverly Whipple, Ph.D., RN, FAAN, has conducted numerous studies and research on the suppression of pain by genital orgasmic and non-orgasmic self-stimulation in women. Refer to the Appendix C to obtain more on her research and studies.

MISSING THE BLESSING

Some women do not achieve orgasms due to physical, psychological, and/or emotional challenges. Steps for resolving these challenges have been listed in various chapters of this Workbook. Some women never experience orgasm due to improper stimulation or lack of knowledge on how to receive sexual pleasure.

Some women vocally express the pleasure of orgasms they never had. In other words, they *lie* about receiving an orgasm. It is a sin to fake an orgasm. *Why?* Because faking is lying, being hypocritical, phony, and deceptive. An open door of lying leads to other falsehoods. Wives lie not only about having an orgasm, but when asked, *"How was it?"* the response reflects pleasure. Sin begets sin! Lying is an abomination to God (Proverbs 6:17).

WHAT YOU MUST DO IF YOU HAVE FAKED ORGASMS

- ❧ Acknowledge, confess, and repent of it to yourself and to God (1 John 1:9).
- ❧ Identify and resolve the root cause of why you have been lying (sinning).
- ❧ Go and sin no more (John 5:14)!
- ❧ Apply the *sexplosion* lovemaking techniques outlined in this Workbook to begin *sexperiencing* and enjoying *sexplosive* orgasms.

VARIOUS METHODS TO ORGASMIC *SEXPLOSIONS*

There are a variety of methods to obtain orgasms. Here are few considerations.

Clitoral

God uniquely made the clitoris as your highly sensitive organ for the sole purpose of sexual delight. "Clitoris" is a Greek word with the root meaning of "key" or "kleis." Oftentimes the clitoris is the only key to some women's orgasmic *sexplosion*s. *Sexperimenting* is required to identify how to use this "key" to open the door to your orgasmic *sexplosions*. To bring about multiple *sexplosive* orgasms, the clitoris can be stimulated many ways, such as through intercourse, through oral or manual stimulation, with love toys, etc.

Non-genital

Non-genital is an orgasm achieved with no genital contact. Non-genital orgasms can be received when you are mentally already *sex-*

cited through erotic thoughts or a high sex drive to the point where any form of physical stimulation sends you over the edge into orgasm. A non-genital orgasm can be achieved by simply, yet passionately, kissing; by having your breasts or nipples kissed or sucked, thighs caressed or licked, or ears or neck nuzzled; or by stimulating any erogenous area.

Full-body

This is a *sexplosive* orgasm felt throughout the whole body. It is often *sexperienced* when there is a strong emotional relationship between you and your husband as well as when you are overwhelmingly feeling sensual and sexual and mentally make love.

Simultaneous

Simultaneous orgasm is when you and your husband have an orgasm at the same time. This requires *sexperimenting* to identify the best techniques and positions that can bring the two of you to have simultaneous orgasms. This may be difficult to achieve. It should never be the goal in lovemaking because it can become a distraction to fully enjoying intimacy.

2 In 1

This orgasm is achieved from simultaneous stimulation of more than one erogenous zone. *Sexperiment* to identify what particularly sensitive body parts, when stimulated at the same time as your vagina or clitoris, take you to a higher level of orgasmic *sexplosion*. For example: Nibbling on your breast might give you a slight orgasm, and combining that with stroking your G-Spot can bring on another orgasm at the same time. These two orgasms together can *sexhilarate* the lovemaking sparkle to an orgasmic *sexplosion*.

Multiple Orgasms

Just because your husband had an orgasm or you had one does not mean lovemaking has to end. Your husband can continue to make love to you via a potpourri of lovemaking methods until you beg for *mercy* from being on a pleasurable, intensified, orgasmic, thrilling sensation. Multiple orgasms can be:

- ❦ *Interval.* Interval orgasms occur two to three minutes apart. Your level of sexual arousal may peak up and down between orgasms.
- ❦ *Consecutive.* Consecutive orgasms occur one right after the other. The consecutive orgasms are separated by mere seconds with no diminishment of sexual arousal. Some women experience this as one long orgasm with spasms of varying intensity.

Multiple Orgasm Technique:

To achieve multiple orgasms requires skill and *"how to"* knowledge. To receive multiple orgasms may require *sexperimenting* and a lifetime of practicing. Do not ever give up practicing! Forcing your husband to give you multiple orgasms can be stressful for him if you do not receive them. Playing and laughing yield a relaxed, loving atmosphere. Here are some considerations for your husband to *sexperiment* with to take you to multiple orgasmic heaven:

- ❦ Consider experiencing your first orgasm via oral love-making. Why first? Oral lovemaking more fully arouses the female genitalia. Continue oral stimulation to achieve additional orgasm. For the specific *how to* knowledge of oral stimulation, refer to the section on *Lovemaking Method—Oral Stimulation* in this chapter. After oral stimulation, *sexperiment* to achieve additional orgasms via manual stimulation. If no orgasm via manual stimulation, revert to oral stimulation for orgasms.

💗 *Sexperiment* to achieve 2 in 1 orgasms through simultaneous stimulation of manual love play and oral lovemaking. Try achieving 3 in 1 orgasms by combining manual, oral, and anal love play stimulation. Your husband can test his dexterity and coordination skill by pleasuring you with four or more simultaneous orgasms by stimulating you in all of your orgasmic and erogenous areas. Thereafter, he can either revert to oral or manual stimulation, or a combination of the two simultaneously, with the addition of love toys. Maintain a pattern of the varied simultaneous love techniques and methods as long as desired and orgasms are received, or husband tolerates, or you do not give out! Conclude with intercourse in a position that allows stimulation of the clitoris.

After receiving an orgasm, constant clitoral stimulation may be painful; therefore, it may be necessary to relieve clitoral stimulation until a period of recovery and then continue stimulation.

TIPS FOR INTENSIFYING ORGASMS

Here are a few practical tips to get your love volcano to boil, overflow, and then *sexplode:*

💗 Make love mentally.
💗 Focus on and enjoy the sensational messages your body is receiving within your nipples, clitoris, and other pleasure zones. Enjoy what you are feeling.
💗 Squeeze your PC *love* muscle during orgasm to intensify and to extend the duration of an orgasm.
💗 Know what turns you on or off and communicate these triggers to your husband.
💗 Know the best stimulation method to include stroking, licking, sucking, nibbling, teasing, and flicking of the

tongue for you to reach orgasm. *Sexperiment* to learn what intensifies your orgasms: French kissing, eye locking, tongue pulling, squeezing or biting of the nipples, using certain positions or a specific lovemaking method or maneuver, etc.

❤ Know the type of stimulation you need, such as slow and gentle or hard and fast, etc.

Prayer for Sexhilarating Sexplosions

Father God in Heaven,

God, You are welcome in our love chambers. God, I praise You for the sexhilarating, sexciting, sensations I sexperience within my mind and body.

Thank You, God, for sexual intimacy. Thank You for designing every intricate part of my being to enjoy sexual intimacy. I want to sexperience a deeper sexual intimate level with my husband in my mind and my body. God, I surrender myself to You to break down any barriers, inhibitions, or negative aspects of lovemaking I may have. I want to give to my husband and receive everything from my husband. Help me to be free to verbally sexpress my sexhilarating sexplosions to my husband.

I want to know and enjoy every possible way I can make love to my husband and my husband can make love to me.

In Jesus' Name I pray,
Amen!

LOVEMAKING METHOD—
MANUAL STIMULATION

Manual stimulation is the direct stimulation of your clitoris, vaginal, anus, and other erogenous love zones using your husband's hands and fingers to bring you to multiple orgasmic *sexplosions.* Many women have multiple orgasms via manual stimulation of the clitoris. Manual stimulation should be enjoyed *with* every method of lovemaking for you to *sexperience* multiple orgasmic *sexplosions.*

TIPS FOR MANUAL STIMULATION

God has designed your *bed of pleasure* with many erogenous areas. So it is imperative for you and your husband to identify these areas. He needs to know where all parts of your sexual pleasure zones are located and what they look like. Proper technique is very important for manual stimulation. As you and your husband begin to refine manual stimulation techniques that awaken your orgasmic sensation, discard old ineffective stimulation techniques that have not done anything for you in the past. Here are a few important tips and techniques for manual stimulation.

ALWAYS relax

You should be mentally and physically relaxed. If you are tense, you cannot enjoy the pleasure of lovemaking. You should allow your husband to massage your body to relax the tension away. If you are fearful, remember God did not give you a spirit of fear, but of power, love, and a sound mind (2 Timothy 1:7). Use the gift of power and a sound mind to overcome fear and freely give love to and receive love from your husband. You have a wonderfully designed body; share it with your husband.

ALWAYS use lubrication

Do not stimulate without lubrication. A lot of lubrication is a must! Lack of or an insufficient amount of lubrication will make the clitoris painful, uncomfortable, and sore. For continual pleasure, do not allow the stimulating object, whether hand, finger, or love toy, to become dry. Use a good lubricant, such as Astroglide®. Some oils, lotions, and lubricating jellies tend to dry out faster and cause friction. Friction may be a powerful pleasure for some. Do not use petroleum jelly products—they are

> *If it feels good, sexpress to him to do it!*

not water soluble, which may be unhealthy if it gets in your vagina or urethra. Water-based lubricants are best for the vaginal area. *Again,* make sure the vaginal area, specifically the clitoris, is very well lubricated.

TECHNIQUES FOR THE VAGINAL AREA

Your husband begins by loving your vulva, herein referred to as the vaginal area or *bed of pleasure*. He can take all the time he wants to *sexperiment* with various types of stimulation: hands, fingers, and/or love toys. Do not get in a hurry. The two of you must relax and enjoy every iota of *sexhilarating* pleasure. Identify what brings you to multiple orgasmic pleasures by *sexperimenting* with various types of repetitive stimulation—fast and slow; hard and soft; up and down; in and out; clockwise and counter clockwise; twisting and thumping; rolling and pulling; slaps and taps; vibrating and circulating; etc. *Sexpress* to your husband *what* you like him to do, *how* you want him to do it, *when* you want him to do it, and *where* you want him to do it!

He should *sexcite* your vaginal area in every way possible. He should make love to every inch of the *bed of pleasure* area. Do not overlook any crack, corner, or crevice. The more he stimulates, the more blood that flows to the area; and the more blood that flows to the area, the greater the sensation. This is the way God so uniquely knitted you together.

He starts by caressing the pubic mound. He presses and massages in gentle circles, from side to side, or back and forth, kneads it like bread, presses the vaginal lips together, vibrates, caresses, squeezes, and strokes them. He moves down to spread open the outer vaginal lips to caress, massage, and stroke the outer perimeter of the inner lips with various stimuli. Then he can spread open the inner vaginal lips and stroll on the inside of the inner lips for you to receive an even more intense electrifying pleasure. Stimulate the pleasure zone of the *U-Delight* (the urethra). While he is stimulating your vaginal area with one hand, he can simultaneously massage the inner thighs, perineum, anus, belly, buttocks, nipples and other erogenous areas with his other hand. Then he can begin to stimulate your vaginal area with one hand and with the other hand he can simultaneously stimulate your perineum area with slow, soft, lightly teasing touches. As your husband is making love to your outer *bed of pleasure* area, he can simultaneously love your inner vagina area by stimulating your G-Spot. For more on G-Spot, refer to *"Other Delights of Lovemaking"* section in this chapter.

TECHNIQUE FOR THE CLITORIS

Proper stimulation technique is very important for clitoral stimulation. Your husband must master the art of loving your clitoris. The way he becomes a *sexpert* is by the two of you learning your sexual anatomy, *sexperimenting* with various stimulation techniques, and you verbalizing to him what is pleasurable as you practice, practice, and practice.

> *You know where his penis is located.*
>
> *Does he know where your clitoris is located?*

God has so uniquely designed the clitoris that some get hard and stand out, yet others may shrink back under the hood, which is its protective covering. Sexual arousal is often a prerequisite to direct clitoral stimulation. It may be uncomfortable for your husband to go directly to the clitoris and stimulate without sexually arousing you via some other means. Initially, the clitoris may be very sensitive to direct stimulation. Therefore, it is important to begin with gentle, slow stimulation to the clitoris and much lubrication.

Your husband can *sexperiment* with a variety of clitoral stimulation techniques to identify what brings you to immense gratification, resulting in multiple manual stimulation *sexplosive* orgasms. It is imperative for you to verbalize to him how to apply continual varied stimulation such as strokes (hard, soft, fast, slow, or up and down); massages (gentle circles, side to side, back and forth, shaking, or vibrating); caresses (clockwise and counterclockwise, twisting, thumping, or tapping); etc. He can also tease the top and bottom sides of the clitoris at the same time.

Upon approaching an orgasm, communicate to your husband the rhythm and stimulation to continue. Changing the pace or stimulation can lessen or intensify the orgasmic pleasure. To prolong or intensify your pleasure, when you feel orgasm approaching, he can move the stimulus from the clitoris to the surrounding areas. This teasing technique can peak your degree of arousal up and down until you are ready to go all the way to a *sexplosive* orgasm. In the midst of an orgasm, take it higher by physically enjoying the pleasure by doing hula-hoop moves with your hips and pelvis and mentally enjoying by focusing on the *sexceptional* pleasure.

Immediately after you have an orgasm via manual stimulation of the clitoris, you may begin to feel a strong *do not touch me anymore* sensation and want to beg for *mercy.* When you experience this non-pleasurable sensation, your husband will need to ease off the clitoris. Let the clitoris recover for a few seconds. But do not stop making love to your other multiplicity of pleasure zones. After a few seconds or minutes of recovery to the clitoris, tell your husband to begin making love to your clitoris again. You must verbalize to your husband the need to redirect stimulation to and from the clitoris—he will not know unless you tell him. Remember, your husband is not all-knowing.

POTPOURRI OF MANUAL STIMULATION

Combine all of the above vaginal and clitoral stimulation techniques simultaneously. He must learn how to stimulate the clitoris and vagina simultaneously while massaging the inner thighs, perineum, anus, belly, buttocks, nipples, and other titillating erogenous zones. You can enhance your orgasmic pleasure by simultaneously using love toys, anal arousal, or other pleasures you desire. Upon recovery of the clitoris orgasm, resume with stimulation to the vaginal area. Continue this potpourri of stimulation until you run out of orgasms (or at least have fun trying!). Include stimulation of the *U-Delight* and G-Spot in this joy divine. For a *little heaven on earth,* give a two-finger massage—one in the vagina and one in the anus or the perineum area.

POSITIONS

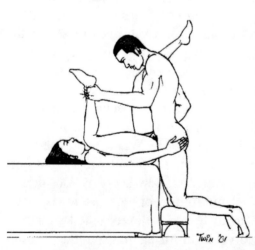

Positional Illustration P–02

If lying on your back, use many pillows to elevate your hips/pelvic area. To allow your husband to spend quality and, of course, quantity time in your *bed of pleasure,* make sure he is comfortable and in a good, relaxed position. Ideal positions for manual stimulation are those that allow your husband to be comfortable and free to use both hands without straining or tiring. This ideal manual stimulation position can conclude in intercourse while simultaneously stimulating the clitoris. Positional Illustration P–02 is shown.

OTHER CONSIDERATIONS

Never use the same hand or fingers he stimulated your anal area with to stimulate your vagina. Make sure hands, fingers, and nails are cleaned. Nails should be trimmed, not sharp, with no hang nails. Keep handy antibacterial hand cleaners or wipes to clean hands and fingers. When combining oral stimulation with manual stimulation, use an edible lubricant.

LOVEMAKING METHOD— ORAL STIMULATION

Oral lovemaking is the use of the mouth and tongue to stimulate the genital area to orgasmic pleasure. Oral lovemaking is not limited to just receiving oral-genital contact (i.e., cunnilingus—to the female genitals), but should encompass every part of the body, from head to toe, not missing any part.

Praise God, it is through Christ Jesus that your marriage bed is undefiled (Hebrews 13:4). If you are advancing to this point in the Workbook and have failed to receive the freedom of God's Word regarding various methods of lovemaking, including oral stimulation, you are exhorted to return to the beginning and study the biblical principles of sexual intimacy. If you have a lack of knowledge of God's Word regarding what is acceptable and unacceptable in the marriage bed, you must abide in the Word to know the sexual freedom you have in Christ. It is only through abiding in the Word of God that you will be set free from wrong beliefs and teachings regarding sexual intimacy (John 8:31–32). What God has said is *"very good"* you must not identify as *"dirty"* or *"nasty"* (Genesis 1:31; 1 Timothy 4:4). What God has declared as *"undefiled"* you must not declare as *"sinful"* or *"defiled"* (Hebrews 13:4). If you are weak in your faith, hear the word of God that will set you free from all falsehoods (Romans 10:17; John 8:32). For more biblical insight on abiding in the Word, make sure you read and study this entire Workbook.

TECHNIQUE

As with all methods of lovemaking, you must relax. The intensity of your orgasm is dependent on your ability to be able to relax and *"let go."* Let go by knowing that there is nothing *"nasty," "dirty,"* or *"disgusting"* about your *bed of pleasure.* Let go by making love mentally. Let go by enjoying what your body is *sexperiencing.* Let go by knowing your most intensive orgasmic *sexplosion* can be through oral stimulation of the clitoris. Let go by knowing the clitoris is the "key" that God so fearfully and wonderfully made for your sole orgasmic pleasure. Allow your husband to orally stimulate your God-given "key" for your mind-shattering, body-quivering, and heart-fluttering orgasmic release.

Proper technique is very important for making love orally. To the surprise of many, making love orally requires practice, patience, and a lot of intimate communication. Many of the oral stimulation techniques are the same as manual stimulation, which are outlined in the previous *"Lovemaking Methods—Manual Stimulation"* in this chapter. Change the listed tips for manual to oral and apply the same stimulation and technique.

Orgasmic pleasure through oral stimulation is usually not found solely in using the tongue to thrust in and out of the vagina like a penis. The pleasure is in receiving the right kind of lick, kiss, nibble, stroke, flick, and suck to your clitoris or to your entire vaginal area. The proper orgasmic stimulation requires you to verbalize to your husband whether to love you hard, slow, fast, with up and down strokes, in gentle circles, side to side, and/or clockwise or counterclockwise movements. Consider the following types of oral stimulation:

The candle flick method

He uses the tip of his tongue as a candle flame. Think about a candle flame flickering in the wind. That is how he moves his tongue rapidly around the sides of your clitoris, above and below it, around the urethra, in the corner and crevices of your inner vaginal lips, and in every part of your *bed of pleasure*. The rapid flicks are similar to the flame of a candle blowing.

The ice cream lick method

He uses the flat of his tongue with long, slow, upward and side to side motions, just like licking ice cream on a cone.

The swirl method

He uses the tip or flat of his tongue to make swirling, circling, rotating, and twisting motions all over your *bed of pleasure*. Also for added pleasure, he can use the back or underside of his tongue to stimulate you.

The potpourri method

Enjoy the combination of the candle flick, ice cream lick, and swirl methods. The TNT or dynamite sensation of this *sexplosion* requires you to *sexpress* to your husband the *what, when, where,* and *how* of oral stimulation you desire.

While loving you orally, your husband can vary the stimulation to the clitoral area by inserting his finger(s) into the vagina and stimulating your G-spot. When his tongue or mouth gets tired, he can incorporate manual stimulation, the use of his hand, fingers, nose, lips, a love toy, etc.

POSITIONS

The ideal position for your husband to love you orally is where you place your *bed of pleasure* over his face. Positional Illustration P–03, shown here, allows you to put your pleasure zones *where* you want him to make love to you orally. You control the speed, movement, pressure, and pleasure of your own arousal. Just do not get so *sexcited* that

Positional Illustration P–03

he cannot breathe. *You would not want to explain to the paramedics how you smothered him.* The position is also ideal because your husband can be comfortable and not put forth much effort or strain. *Sexperiment* with various positions to identify which position gives you ultimate oral pleasure.

BANQUET OF LOVE

Have a banquet in your *lovemaking chambers*, the location where you make love. You may make a spread of scrumptious delights all over your body for your husband to enjoy. Be creative. Try foods that do not require you to spend time chewing. Use quickly dissolvable foods or items requiring a lot of sucking or licking for added pleasure such as peanut butter, powdered sugar, honey, or jam. Try ice cubes that are not directly from the freezer. Let him enjoy you *au naturel,* or in other words, just plain! Keep in mind that oil-based foods and animal fats can tear the latex in a condom. Use towels underneath you or on top of the surface for easy cleanup.

"For everything God made is good" (1 Timothy 4:4).

Freedom in Christ Jesus!

Father God in Heaven,

Where the Spirit of the Lord is, there is liberty (2 Corinthians 3:17). I am free in Christ to enjoy my husband. I will no longer walk in the deceit of the world, false teaching, and lies of the enemy regarding the marriage bed. Thank You that through the new and living covenant with Jesus Christ, I am free from obeying the old law, and through Him I can have all the wonderful sexual pleasures designed by God (Hebrews 8:7–13; 10:20). I rejoice that You have declared my marriage bed to be undefiled (Hebrews 13:4). Therefore, I will enjoy every aspect of sexual pleasure with my husband in the freedom I have through Christ Jesus. Thank You, God, that You designed every intricate part of my body for our sexual pleasure and that every part of my body is for my husband's pleasure (1 Corinthians 7:4).

In Jesus' Name I pray,
Amen!

LOVEMAKING METHOD—
ANAL STIMULATION

One of the ways that Satan has so cleverly destroyed the marriage bed is through false teachings, wrong beliefs, and a lack of knowledge. Christians must abide in the Word of God, which gives you His truths over the lies of Satan. This section of the Workbook, as with all sections, presents a biblical foundation for enjoying all God has given you through Christ Jesus. You are encouraged not to take a shortcut through the Workbook by starting with this section. If you have omitted the previous chapters, go back and begin from the beginning so you can abide in the Word and be free in Christ Jesus to enjoy anal lovemaking.

God designed sexual pleasure for the husband and wife. God condemns sex between two people of the same sex—male with male or female with female—and those outside of the marriage covenant. As with everything God has designed, Satan has taken every aspect of sex and misused it between same-sex people (homosexuals) or between any two people outside of marriage. God never designed sex to be between two people of the same sex but only between a husband and wife in the marital covenant. Under the new covenant of Christ, the marriage bed is undefiled (Hebrews 13:4)

> *Thank You, God, that every part of my body belongs to my husband! Thank You that I can enjoy sexplosive pleasure throughout my whole body.*
>
> *1 Corinthians 7:4*

and every aspect of your body is for your husband's pleasure (1 Corinthians 7:4). Anal love is not excluded in this pleasure.

God designed your anus to have multiple nerve endings, just as the clitoris has multiple nerve endings. God situated your anus in the heart of your sexual *bed of pleasure* zones, to neither be overlooked nor rejected. What God has designed as "very good" (Genesis 1:31; 1 Timothy 4:4) do not declare it as bad or unacceptable. Stop allowing erroneous beliefs and teachings to deny you of sexual intimacy pleasures.

Anal lovemaking involves the sexual gratification of arousal and pleasure to the anus through either intercourse and/or love play. Anal intercourse is when penis is inserted into or penetrates the anus. Anal love play is the stimulation of anus with the finger or a love toy.

CONCERNS OF ANAL STIMULATION

Making love to the anal area is a concern for many people. Some concerns are comfort, pleasure, and hygiene.

Comfort

Implementing all the anal lovemaking tips and techniques listed in this Workbook should decrease any discomfort or uneasiness. Anal love play can be *sextremely sexceptionally sexcellent* when there is no sexual anxiety or fears, general marital relationship insecurities, or domination or power concerns of the husband (or you). If your husband feels anal intercourse or making love in a rear-entry position is a means of expressing power or domination, this concern must be addressed through open and honest communication. Abusive domination has no place in the marriage bed. As with any form of lovemaking, whether oral sex, intercourse, or manual stimulation, abusive sexual behavior can occur where there is a lack of honor and respect.

Pleasure

Knowing *how to* make anal love results in the *sexhilarating* pleasure to the wife. Many have tried anal intercourse, yet due to lack of knowing *"how to"* found it to be non-pleasurable. Anal lovemaking requires knowledge; thus the purpose of the third part of this Workbook. Once you *sexperience* the awesome pleasure, you will regret not *sexperimenting* with anal lovemaking earlier in your marriage.

Hygiene

Your husband can use a condom for his penis, or a finger cot or a thin latex glove to cover his fingers, or anal love toys in place of his penis or finger. Not to minimize the importance of hygiene, cleanliness is important in every form of lovemaking, including oral sex, manual stimulation, intercourse, and anal stimulation. Diseases and infections are not limited to anal lovemaking; therefore, precautionary hygiene methods should always be taken. Concerns you have regarding anal lovemaking should be addressed with your personal physician. See tips on washing in this section.

WHY ANAL LOVEMAKING?

Anal lovemaking can be enjoyed when you are on your menstrual cycle, are pregnant, are experiencing an illness, etc.

Anal lovemaking can be *sextremely sexhilarating* and satisfying for both husband and wife.

Husbands are *sexcited* by the tightness of the anus, which gives him more stimulation and *sexplosive* orgasm.

Husbands enjoy the voyeurism of anal intercourse because he can watch the thrusting action.

TIPS FOR ANAL LOVEMAKING

Proper technique is very important for anal lovemaking. The most important aspect of learning any new technique is *sexperimenting.* *Sexperiment* with a progression of anal love play to anal intercourse. Here are a few important tips and techniques for anal lovemaking:

ALWAYS use lubrication

Do not stimulate the anus without lubrication. A lot of lubrication is a must! No lubrication will make it painful, uncomfortable, and sore, just as when loving the vagina or clitoris. To *sexperience* continual pleasure, do not allow the penis or stimulating finger or toy become dry. Use a good lubricant, such as Astroglide®, or an oil-based lube. Some lotions and lubricating jellies tend to dry out faster and cause friction.

ALWAYS be sextremely sexually aroused

The most common mistake is approaching anal lovemaking without prior stimulation or sexual arousal. Before anal lovemaking, you must be sexually aroused and at the brink of an orgasm and preferably have already experienced multiple orgasms through some other method of lovemaking. Being highly aroused helps keep your mental focus on lovemaking and not the thought of anal love. Also, if you are at the brink of an orgasm, anal love may escalate the orgasm to more profound *sexhilarating sexplosions*. Remember, do not approach anal lovemaking *"cold turkey,"* meaning without being *sextremely* aroused.

ALWAYS relax

Anal lovemaking should be approached when you are at the brink of an orgasm. At the brink of an orgasm is when you are most relaxed and not tensed. Relaxation and pleasure are what you want when you begin anal lovemaking. As with any form of lovemaking, pain will occur if you are not relaxed. You should concentrate on relaxing your anal muscles. To alleviate discomfort, do not tense. Focus on the pleasurable bodily sensations you are receiving while your husband makes love to you orally or via manual stimulation of your other erogenous areas. Allow your mind to enjoy the pleasures. Breathe, relax, and anticipate the bodily volcanic *sexhilarating sex-*

plosions. If you tense with love pleasure to your vagina, hold off on anal love play until you learn to relax and enjoy every aspect of lovemaking. Incorporate the tips in the section on *"Mental Sexplosion"* in Chapter 9.

ALWAYS wash

Due to the opposite chemical nature of the rectum and vagina, never have vaginal intercourse or stimulation after anal stimulation unless the penis, finger, or love toy has been thoroughly washed. Wash the anus and surrounding area beforehand. Dr. LeeRoy McCurley, a board-certified family practioner, stresses the importance of the male always washing himself thoroughly with warm, soapy water after anal intercourse to avoid an infection on the head of the penis.

Always use the hand, finger, or other love toy that has *not* been used in the anus in your vaginal area. Nails of lovemaking fingers should be very short without hangnails. Since you never know when you may desire anal love, keep a nailbrush handy, at the sink or in the shower, for your husband to clean his nails when he washes his hands. Always keep antibacterial hand cleansers and wipes handy when making love.

ALWAYS sexpress

The joy of anal lovemaking is intensified when there is erotic, loving communication between you and your husband. To *sexperience* the ultimate anal *sexplosive* pleasure, it is imperative for you to communicate to your husband during lovemaking. If there is disharmony in the marital relationship, it will manifest in the bed. If there is a lack of open and honest communication outside of the bedroom, there will be no open and honest communication in the bed. Every form of lovemaking requires you and your husband to be free to *sexpress* your likes and dislikes. Focus on building your marital relationship to enhance your lovemaking in the bedroom.

TECHNIQUE FOR <u>FIRST</u> TIME ANAL LOVE PLAY RENDEZVOUS

It is imperative for you to incorporate the anal lovemaking tips in this section. Your husband should approach anal love play *after* you are *sextremely* aroused *and* at the brink of an orgasm. While simultaneously stimulating your other erogenous areas including your clitoris, he gently and slowly massages with light, teasing strokes and touches around your outer anal area. He can use soft feather-like tease touches to the perineum with back-and-forth or circular motions. He can tease you with feathers, fur, or scarf-type material.

> Anal love play need not mean *anal intercourse.*

To *sexperience* the ultimate level of pleasure, you must verbally *sexpress* to your husband the type of stimulation you desire. *Sexperiment* with various types of repetitive stimulation to your outer anal area—fast and slow; hard and soft; up and down; clockwise and counterclockwise; twisting and thumping; rolling and pulling; slaps and taps; vibrating and circulating motions, and other creative titillating ideas you may have.

TECHNIQUE FOR THE <u>SECOND</u> ANAL LOVE PLAY RENDEZVOUS

On your second anal love play rendezvous, begin by applying the techniques listed above in *"First Time Anal Love Play Rendezvous."* As you are relaxed and are enjoying the pleasure, your husband will gently and slowly enter just the tip of his pinky (little) finger in your anus. He should *not* apply any form of stimulation, just allow the finger to rest in your *anus* until you become acquainted with the sensation of his finger inside of you. When he places his finger inside your anus, the anus will naturally contract. Consciously relax. Only after you have relaxed and recognize the sensation of his finger, he should begin to use slow, gentle, circular, vibrating motions or whatever you prefer to *sexcite* you. Simultaneously apply the anal love making techniques in the first and second rendezvous outlined above.

TECHNIQUE FOR THE <u>THIRD</u> ANAL LOVE PLAY RENDEZVOUS

On your third anal love play rendezvous, begin with the techniques listed above in the *"First and Second Anal Love Play Rendezvous."* As you are relaxed and enjoying the pleasure, your husband will gently and slowly insert his entire pinky finger. Consciously relax. With his entire pinky finger inserted inside the anus, he will use slow, gentle, circular, come-here, vibrating motions or whatever you prefer. Simultaneously apply the lovemaking techniques for the

> *What God has designed as "very good," do not declare it as bad or unacceptable.*
> Genesis 1:31; 1 Timothy 4:4

"First and Second Anal Love Play Rendezvous." Your husband should give slow, shallow, gentle thrusts with his finger. You should direct the depth and speed of thrusting. For additional intensified pleasure, rub together the anal and vaginal walls simultaneously: one finger on one hand inserted in the vagina and another finger on the other hand inserted in the anus, rubbing the tip of the two inserted fingers together. Stroke the rectal wall closest to the vagina where there are multiple nerve endings. Before advancing to anal intercourse, work up to inserting more than one finger.

TECHNIQUE FOR EXPERIENCING AN ANAL INTERCOURSE *SEXPLOSION*

As you progress with the pleasure and relaxation of anal finger love play, you will soon be ready for his throbbing penis or a love toy to enter your dynamic anus. Let your husband know when you are ready to *sexperience* the sensation of his penis stroking your anal nerve endings. Ultimate anal intercourse pleasure is enjoyed after you have mastered the first through third love play rendezvous techniques outlined.

Enjoy the pleasure of *sexperimenting* with different anal love making positions: standing, sitting, lying, squatting, etc. Choose a position that will allow you to be in control of movement and depth; see Positional Illustration P–04 shown here. Identifying the right anal lovemaking position helps aids in angling the penis through the anus. Not all positions will allow for deep penetration. Try various anal lovemaking positions that allow simultaneous stimulation of other erogenous zones to bring you to orgasmic *sexplosions.*

Positional Illustration P–04

While incorporating the first through third anal love play rendezvous techniques with an excessively lubricated penis, slowly, gently, and gradually massage the tip of his penis into your anus. He must continue to stimulate your other erogenous areas while loving your anus. Penetration will be slow and should not be rushed. Be patient. Penetrate approximately an inch every fifteen seconds. Full penetration may not occur the first time. Learn to relax and enjoy the sensation of the amount of penis received. Get familiar with the pressure sensation.

Expect full penetration to take some minutes. If full penetration is not enjoyed during the first anal intercourse rendezvous, do not become frustrated; try on another occasion when the two of you are ready. Once entrance is established with the penis, penetration or thrusting will not be as vigorous as it is during vaginal intercourse, but you can relax and enjoy the fullness of his penis inside. Move slowly. You must lead on depth and speed of penis penetration. If you find this discomforting, stop.

Applying all of these *sexperimenting* techniques is a must for anal love play and anal intercourse lovemaking. If after *sexperimenting* three times with different positions and amounts of lubrication, anal intercourse (with the penis) continues to be uncomfortable for you, revert back to the first through third rendezvous techniques outlined or a vibrating anal love toy for pleasure. When using love toys, make sure the object has a flared base so it will not slip into the rectum and become difficult to recover.

OTHER CONCERNS

Many desire to *sexplore* the pleasure of anal stimulation, yet they want to know the health concerns. Dr. McCurley reports, "The major concern of anal sex between a man and a woman is trauma to the anal sphincter, which is a ring of muscle responsible for the integrity of the anal opening." Dr. McCurley emphasizes, "Care should be taken as to use an appropriate amount of lubrication here to avoid tearing the anal sphincter which can result in incontinence. This means that control of passing feces is lost."

"Medical concerns of bacteria entering the urethra of a male do exist but are not looked on as harmful," states Dr. McCurley. "Of course," he says, "this depends on the type of bacteria. Assuming we are not talking about bacteria which are associated with several types of venereal diseases, the bacteria rarely causes any harm to the male because of the length of the urethra. This distance from the bladder makes getting a bladder infection more difficult as the bacteria have a longer area to travel to set up an infectious site. Unlike the female," explains Dr. McCurley, "simple anatomy protects the male from having a problem here. Usually most bacteria is flushed out when the male voids, further reducing his chances of a problem developing."

OTHER CONSIDERATIONS

Sexperiment to master this anal *sexplosion* technique: Your husband makes love to you with his thumb vibrating in your anus, his finger in your vagina stroking your G-Spot, and his mouth sucking your clitoris. Another alternative to anal penis penetration is to try the crease of your buttocks. It may feel a lot like vaginal intercourse to your husband. Whether you are on your hands and knees or stomach, your husband guides his penis between the crease of your buttocks, squeezing them together to make a tunnel. He can thrust in and out of the tunnel for pleasure. Another alternative is the use of a small (in diameter), flexible, vibrating anal love toy to help you relax and to enhance anal pleasure. Allow your husband to *sexperiment* with a vibrating love toy to relax your anus and to enhance the *sexhilarating* sensation in your anus and against your vaginal wall.

LOVEMAKING METHOD— INTERCOURSE

Intercourse, also known as coitus, is the sexual pleasure of the penis inserted into the vagina. Intercourse is the only physical lovemaking method that brings forth the reproduction of children, also called procreation. It is a special moment when the penis meets the vagina. Intercourse can be an earth-shattering experience traveling throughout your body as the two of you become one flesh. Many believe lovemaking always involves intercourse. There are many ways to sexually express love one to another. This section outlines, not in any particular order, various important factors of intercourse that are not often considered.

ORGASMS

For the penis to enter the vagina is not a complex matter. However, for the wife to experience *sexplosive* orgasmic pleasure during intercourse involves much more skill. There are many factors involved for the wife to have an intercourse orgasm. Here are some factors that must be considered for the wife to enjoy *sexplosive* orgasmic pleasure during intercourse.

To experience an orgasm during a *quickie* rendezvous is to be already sexually aroused to the point of orgasm. When you are highly sexually aroused, during *quickie* intercourse, your husband can manually stimulate your clitoris to *sexcite* you to simultaneous climax with him. It is best to be at the brink of orgasm when you have intercourse. Your intercourse orgasm can be even more *sexhilarating* if you have already experienced orgasms via other lovemaking methods. When you are highly aroused and your vaginal love juices are overflowing, this is the time to allow your husband's throbbing penis to enter your *vagina*. Communication is very important to transition from one lovemaking method into intercourse. You must *sexpress* to your husband when you are at the brink of an orgasm and when you want to make the transition to intercourse. He cannot read your mind, and he does not know when you are at the brink of an orgasm.

Frustration and expectations are factors most couples overlook regarding intercourse. Frustration and expectation should not be in the marriage bed. Neither you nor your husband should get upset or frustrated when you do not have an orgasm via intercourse. If you do not experience an orgasm during intercourse lovemaking is not over. Your husband can continue to make love to you with manual stimulation, stimulation with toys, or however you desire. Refer to Chapter 9, *"Orgasmic Sexplosion,"* for more on orgasms.

It is possible, but not likely, that you will experience an orgasm if you go immediately into intercourse lovemaking without any prior stimulation. This is a common factor that is not considered by many couples. It can be even more difficult for you to have an intercourse orgasm if you are not aroused and your husband is thrusting hard and vigorously. That is why it is important for you to have had pre-intercourse orgasms or excessive foreplay that will bring you to the brink of orgasm then enter into intercourse to bring about an intercourse orgasm.

To go from brink of orgasm to orgasm involves incorporating: making love mentally, squeezing your PC *love* muscle, enhancing your thrust patterns, transitioning into a lovemaking position that is conducive to orgasmic pleasure, and your husband simultaneously stimulating your clitoris and other erogenous areas.

The other common factor about intercourse is that many wives do not like intercourse because their husband ejaculates before they can have an orgasm. The simplest solution for you and your husband to enjoy your sexual differences is outlined in the *"Distinctively Different"* section and *"The Joy of Trade Off"* section in Chapter 8. Simultaneous orgasms should not be the goal of lovemaking because it can bring about frustration when one spouse orgasms before the other.

If your husband ejaculates quickly, is it due to deprivation or to him being in a sexual drought? If he is in a sexual drought because you have been depriving him, he perhaps will ejaculate quickly. Switching to multiple positions, changing thrusting rhythms, or implementing any other techniques may not prevent quick ejaculation if it is a result of him being sexually deprived. Stop depriving him and begin to increase the frequency of intercourse. Keep in mind that quick ejaculation may be a natural tendency for him; if so, the *"Trade Off"* lovemaking method is for you to enjoy.

If you would like to try prolonging intercourse, you can *sexperiment* with the technique of switching to different lovemaking positions and with varying thrusting patterns. To alleviate arousal frustration, you and your husband must agree when to make positional changes. To try to prolong intercourse, shift from one position to another during lovemaking. The following illustrations are examples of transitioning from one position to another. These positions will limit your ability to thrust and rock; therefore, lovemaking will be prolonged. Begin lovemaking in P–05. This intimate seated position allows for body closeness so you may enjoy kissing and caressing one another. When you both desire, you can transition to P–06. If you like, transition back into the beginning position, P–05. Props may be needed to add comfort. When attempting any new position, it is important for you to apply the *sexperimenting* tips outlined in

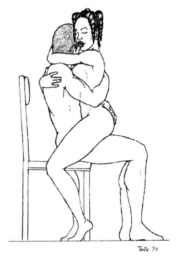

Positional Illustration P–05

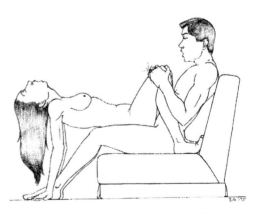

Positional Illustration P–06

"*Becoming a Sexpert*" and "*It's in the Position*" sections of Chapter 9. For more on lovemaking positions, obtain the *Sexplosion in Marriage: God's Gift of Intimacy in Lovemaking Positions,* another marriage resource book in the Sexplosion in Marriage Series ™.

THRUSTING

There is a skill to thrusting that can give you pleasure, provide an orgasmic release, and prolong intercourse. For *quickie* lovemaking, the hard, deep, and fast thrusting movement can lead to ejaculation in minutes, if not seconds. Keep in mind that if your husband is in a sexual drought, quick ejaculation may occur. Quick ejaculation may be a natural tendency for your husband; see "*Distinctively Different*" in Chapter 8.

To learn how to prolong intercourse through thrusting requires *sexperimenting* to identify the best pattern. Thrusting stimulation strokes can include in and out, side to side, circling, and a combination thereof. Most rear-entry thrusting positions with proper body angling can enhance the penis stroking the G-Spot. It is important to identify the thrusting patterns that are pleasing to both you and your husband. Some examples of thrusting patterns are:

- 💓 *Four Slow, Two Fast.* The depth of penetration varies in the slow thrusts from shallow to deep. The two fast thrusts are deep.
- 💓 *Three Shallow, One Deep.* Enter only two or three inches into the vagina, which is supposed to create a vaginal vacuum. The deep thrust forces the air out of the vagina, making the penis feel more tightly held. You may feel G-Spot stimulation from the shallow thrusts.

MENSTRUAL CYCLE

William H. Masters, M.D., and Virginia E. Johnson, leading researchers of the anatomy and physiology of human sexual response, conducted a study on women having sex during their menstrual cycle. Their research found only ten percent of 331 women objected to sex during their menstrual cycle. Most women desired sex during the later half of their cycle. This research indicates you are not odd or abnormal if your sexual desire peaks during or pre- or post-menstruation.

According to gynecologists, this peak is because the rush of blood flow to the pelvic area during menstruation is the same as the rush of blood flow during sexual excitement. This similarity sends the same signals to the brain. As a result of blood building up or becoming congested in your pelvic area, experiencing an orgasm may relieve the buildup or pressure. Orgasms relieve the tension in the pelvic area because the blood flow is redirected from the pelvic area to other areas throughout your body. Other ongoing human sexuality studies indicate that the brain releases chemicals called "endorphins," which are responsible for the sensation of pleasure and, when released, reduce pain.

Some additional tips for sexual intimacy during menstruation include, but are not limited to:

- ♀ Using condoms for the penis or love toy.
- ♀ Making love under water such as in the bathtub or shower.
- ♀ Putting large, dark-colored towels underneath you for easy cleanup.
- ♀ Having wipes or damp towels available.
- ♀ Enjoying a love toy if your husband does not desire intercourse.
- ♀ Removing tampons.

Sharon E. Greggs, M.D., FACOG, a leading obstetrician and gynecologist in Dallas, Texas, suggests the use of a diaphragm to collect the menstrual blood. A diaphragm is a rubber dome-shaped cap that is inserted through the vagina to cover the cervix. She emphasizes to follow the guidelines for using a diaphragm and to "wash thoroughly after use." Diaphragms are prescribed and fitted by your gynecologist for contraceptive purposes.

Consult with your personal gynecologist regarding intercourse during your menstrual cycle.

PUBOCOCCYGEUS (PC) "LOVE" MUSCLE

One of the reasons some women do not experience orgasm during intercourse is due to a lack of knowledge and use of their PC *love* muscle, the Pubococcygeus muscle or "PC" (often referred to in this Workbook as the "PC *love* muscle"). You must learn how to strengthen this PC *love* muscle. A strong PC *love* muscle aids in giving and receiving pleasure during intercourse. Your strong PC *love* muscle can grip, squeeze, and massage your husband's penis as it is thrusting in and out of your vagina.

The following are the benefits of a strong PC *love* muscle:

- ❦ Achieves frequent, longer, bigger, better, and stronger orgasms.
- ❦ Grips and massages the penis to his delight.
- ❦ Contracts around the penis, allowing for greater stimulation and sensation for both husband and wife.
- ❦ Enhances the ability to grip his penis better as you thrust in various lovemaking positions.

SENSATION OF THE PENIS

If during intercourse you do not feel the throbbing sensation of his penis inside your vagina, try the following tips:

- ❦ Increase thrusting and squeeze your PC *love* muscle during thrusting.

- 🍂 Strengthen your PC *love* muscle to create a snug fit of his penis inside your vagina.
- 🍂 If using artificial lubrication, use less.

Sexperiment with various positions where your legs are closer together and positions where your knees are close to your chest versus spread eagle type positions. See Positional Illustration P–07 shown here.

Positional Illustration P–07

VAGINAL DRYNESS

Your natural lubrication may fluctuate depending on many factors such as age, hormones, diet, medicine, and other health conditions. You should discuss vaginal dryness and pain with your personal physician or gynecologist. Although not an exhaustive listing, some additional considerations to identify what may cause vaginal dryness are as follows:

- 🍂 *Substances.* Avoid substances that dry your membranes, such as antihistamines, diuretics, alcohol, and caffeine. These also dry the lining of the vagina, which are membranes.
- 🍂 *Foreplay.* Lack of foreplay or pre-intercourse arousal will not provide sufficient natural lubricants. A lack of natural lubrication can make penetration difficult and painful. Incorporate foreplay to allow an ample supply of natural lubrication to flow.

🍒 *Lubrications.* If natural lubricants are not sufficient, vaginal dryness may occur resulting in pain or discomfort during intercourse. Therefore, it is imperative to use an artificial lubricant to reduce or alleviate the pain or discomfort. Too much lubrication may result in too little friction such that neither of you will feel the penetration or thrusting of his penis. Learn by *sexperimenting* how much lubrication is a good thing.

Sexperiment to identify an artificial lubricant that does not dry out and the brand you prefer, such as Astroglide®, etc. There are water-based, oil-based, and petroleum-based lubricants. Most sexual lubricants are water-based. Water-based are slippery and carry a low risk of causing vaginal problems. Oil-based lubricants are vegetable oils or massage-type oils. Vaseline®, which is petroleum-based, and some other oils may tear condoms.

PAIN DURING INTERCOURSE

Painful intercourse, known as "dispareunia," could be the result of many factors. Sex and medical experts indicate that psychological, physical, and relationship problems may contribute to painful intercourse. Consult with your personal physician or gynecologist regarding any pain or health conditions. Some common causes are:

🍒 Deep thrusting, which can hit the tip of the cervix, resulting in pelvic pain or an uncomfortable feeling. The solution is to identify positions that reduce deep penetration. Select positions that allow for shallower penetration or those where you are in control of the depth of penetration.

🍒 Medical conditions such as endometriosis, a fibroid, pelvic inflammatory disease, bladder infection, or other infections. *Vestibulitis,* which is a swelling of the glands along the vaginal opening, can cause pain. Pain may intensify with the thrusting of the penis if there is a vaginal irritation or infection.

- ❧ Some medications, whether over-the-counter or prescription, may also be the contributor to vaginal dryness, which can cause pain.

- ❧ Vaginal irritation as a result of an allergic reaction to vaginal douches, body sprays, perfumes, deodorants, bath additives, nonoxynol-9 spermicides, etc.

- ❧ *Vaginismus*, which is an involuntary tightening of your vaginal muscles. This condition is thought to be emotional or psychological. Get to the root by identifying the spiritual or psychological cause for why you become tense during sexual intimacy. Until the issue is addressed, try a generous amount of a water-soluble lubricant.

- ❧ If you are nervous or tense about sexual intimacy, you may be consciously or unconsciously tightening your vagina. To enjoy making love, relaxation and mental focus are a must.

- ❧ If you go for long periods without having intercourse, you may experience pain when his penis enters your vagina. Increasing the frequency of lovemaking and using a lubricant may resolve this matter.

Some other common reasons for pain during intercourse may be emotional or psychological, not limited to stress, fear of pregnancy, anger, resentment, or disharmony in the marriage.

OTHER DELIGHTS TO INTENSIFY LOVEMAKING

You should always seek ways to enhance your lovemaking. Never become monotonous. God has given you creative abilities; use them to identify ways you can intensify the *sexcitement* in your marriage bed. Here are some common ways to intensify lovemaking.

BONDAGE

Bondage pleasure is an erotic restraint to you or your husband that intensifies pleasure through delaying gratification. Restraints are used to tie you down and tease you in sexual pleasure.

Tie and tease is most effective when your sexual desire is very strong; therefore, you must communicate to your husband when your sexual desire is high or *sexpress* your desire to be tied and teased. When your sexual desire is high, you may be able to withstand the tease pleasure for a more prolonged time span.

Open communication is a must to discuss guidelines for the bondage thrill of lovemaking. It is important to discuss what activities are acceptable or unacceptable. Bondage should never be about power, control, or abuse. Everything should be fun, playful, erotic, and *sexciting*.

Tie and Tease Techniques

He loosely binds your wrists and/or ankles and adds a blindfold. Do not constrict blood flow. Do not restrain the neck area. You should be able to insert two fingers between the restraint and the body part restrained. Teasing does not have to be to the point of orgasm, but the *sexcitement* is in the ability to peak the level of arousal up and down with strong anticipation of *sexperiencing* an orgasm. He teases you to the brink of orgasm, pulls back, and teases again. He can abruptly stop genital stimulation, then repeat the stop-start method of genital stimulation until you beg for an orgasm. He teases you with kisses, caresses, strokes, and touches all over your entire body. He can use oral or manual techniques or love toys to stimulate you to a higher level of arousal. Slow, prolonged teasing of oral, manual, and thrusting of the tip of the penis stimulation can be a form of intense pleasure.

Tease techniques require skill and practice. Your husband must have previously learned, as a result of you communicating to him, how and where you like to be teased, stroked, licked, kissed, nibbled, and sucked to pleasure. Remember that light bondage can lead to muscle cramps. Do not sustain the experience so long that you are begging for a muscle massage rather than an orgasm.

COITAL DYNAMIC STIMULATION MANEUVERS

Coital dynamics is you changing your genital or body movements during lovemaking to enhance your pleasurable and sensational stimulation. Most women *sexperience* intercourse orgasms through employing these various coital maneuvers. Doing hula-hoop moves (thrusting or gyrating) with your hips and pelvis can aid in *sexperiencing* orgasmic convulsions. You can receive distinct *sexhilarating* sensations simply by shifting your body so the penis strokes your vagina at different angles. Regardless of the position or lovemaking technique or method, coital dynamic maneuvers can intensify lovemaking.

SHOUT IT OUT

The sound of your voice can be stimulating. Saying the same things in the same voice tone over and over again gets old and monotonous. Become seductive! Move your voice up and down through the octaves. Give your husband new sounds to hear.

Make eye contact during lovemaking—do not look away at the point of orgasm. Say *"I love you"* before, during, and after making love.

If you are holding back from freely *sexpressing* the sensation of lovemaking that you are feeling, you are not allowing yourself to *sexperience* all that God has for you. You are depriving yourself of powerful *sexplosions* if you find yourself holding back from verbalizing the pleasure of releasing an orgasm.

Consider your excitement when you experience the thrill of victory in your favorite activity or sports, or when you are on a thrilling amusement ride. When you scream with pleasure, your excitement increases. When you are cheering for or encouraging your favorite team, you really get into the action. This is the type of thrill you should *sexpress* during lovemaking.

You need to stop allowing Satan to steal your *sexplosions* through non-verbal and/or non-body *sexpression*. You must not be deceived by the lies that *good girls* do not make sounds or scream with *sexcitement* because it is *not ladylike* or you will *look silly*. If you are fearful of *sexpressing* yourself or of totally *letting go* sexually, think on this: God has not given you a spirit of fear, but of power, love, and a sound mind (2 Timothy 1:7)!

You must not stifle your *sexplosion*s. God gave you your vocal cords to use, not stifle! Begin to use them for your sexual enjoyment. So, *sexpress* your *sexcitement!* Allow yourself to be free in Christ to enjoy what He has given you. When you focus on the physical *sexcitement,* the mental pleasure, and the orgasmic sensations, you will *shout, cry, holler, scream, grunt, call out your husband's name, verbalize your feelings,* etc. Try it—you will indeed like it!

Take back what you have allowed the enemy to steal, kill, and destroy from you—your *sexhilaration!* Loosen up your vocal cords and shout for joy! If you are shy or still concerned about what your husband might think or say, then tell him about the new you. Share with your husband how you have been in bondage in this area, but you are breaking free from Satan's chains and you are going to *sexperience* all God intended for you. Ask your husband to pray for you and to be supportive of you as you put off the old way of being silent, *good girls don't thinking,* and other falsehoods, and put on your new sensual, *sexplosive, sexciting* vocal cords.

Talk to your husband before, during, and after lovemaking. Be very *sexplicit* in *sexpressing* to him what you want to do to him and what you want him to do to you. Erotic pillow talk can sexually *sexcite* you and your husband and does not have to be vulgar or filthy communication.

FOREPLAY

Foreplay is an integral part of lovemaking. Foreplay does not have to begin at the beginning of lovemaking, but throughout the day to increase the sexual suspense and arousal for what is to come. Build up each other's sexual anticipation. Add elements of surprise every time; be creative. Do not expect your husband to be solely responsible for foreplay.

Foreplay is "play." It should be *sexciting,* suspenseful, fun, and enjoyable. Husbands and wives must learn to take their time and relax, mentally and physically, before, during, and after making love. Foreplay should not be limited to the physical acts of stroking, kissing, blowing, sucking, and licking, but can also include stimulation of all the five senses: sensuous touches, tasteful kisses, enticement by sight, preparation through music, and an erotic smell. Your foreplay desires today may not be the same tomorrow due to emotional factors, hormones, or other circumstances. That is why it is imperative for you to communicate to your husband what you desire. He can become frustrated when he is doing what you asked him to do to arouse or relax you sexually or emotionally, yet you are not responding. He is not a mind reader; he is not *all knowing.* To enhance your foreplay, you must *sexpress* to him *what* you need, *when* you need it, and *how* you need it.

The best love foreplay is *sexpressing* your desires to your husband every time. You may think that takes away the "intimacy." Do not look at the glass as half empty! But, consider that if every time you needed foreplay, you *sexpressed* your arousal needs to him, you would:

🌹 Get your specific desires met.

🌹 Eliminate your husband needing to guess if he is arousing you.

🌹 Speed up arousal by not wasting time with ineffective techniques or stimulation.

🌹 Get the right amount and proper stimulation for natural love juices to flow.

🌹 Help your husband to understand that your needs are truly different every time.

Erogenous Zones. God incorporated erotically sensitive areas throughout your entire body. Because sensitive body parts vary from person to person, it is imperative for you to allow your husband to identify your zones by applying varying sensual stimulation to the whole body from head to toe, not missing any part. Stimulation of erogenous zones can be a part of love play, before, during, and after.

G-SPOT

The G-Spot is not an anatomical area, but a sensitive area along the front vaginal wall that swells when it is massaged and during orgasm. Although called a "spot," it is not a spot but an area. It is a spongy, rough area approximately the size of a bean. Some wives report it takes awhile to find the area, but when located, it is worth the search. Therefore, this area may be difficult to find, and thus difficult to stimulate, so do not become totally G-Spot focused. The G-Spot is named after a German gynecologist, Ernst Grafenberg.

G-Spot Technique

G-Spot is best stimulated *after* you are aroused or have experienced an orgasm via some other method. Always stimulate or search for the G-Spot after *sexperiencing* an orgasm or being highly aroused to the brink of orgasm. The initial stroking of the G-Spot may feel as though you have to urinate; however, this is not the case. So you can relax and not focus on whether or not you are going to urinate. Although it may initially feel like you have to urinate, do not cease stimulation because the sensation can take you into a G-Spot orgasmic high. To ease your mind, empty your bladder before lovemaking.

Intercourse Stimulation

The best intercourse position for stroking the G-Spot is rear entry. Rear entry requires proper angle of your buttock for your husband to stroke the front wall of the vagina with his penis. Additionally, sitting on top of your husband and slightly leaning backwards allows you to angle your body to stroke in the precise area.

Finger Stimulation

(See the G-Spot Illustration shown here). Your husband inserts his finger (preferably the middle finger, which is the longest) into the vagina and gently, yet firmly, strokes the front vaginal wall (belly side) with a *come-hither* gesture. Initially, until you have become *sexperts* in locating your G-Spot area, with his other hand he should 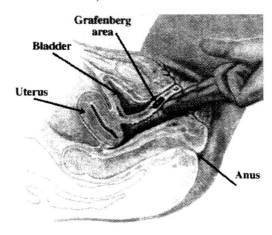 press down on the abdomen just above the pubic bone. The *69* position (with wife on top) is best for finger stimulation.

Stroking of the G-Spot, regardless of position, allows for simultaneous stimulation of other orgasmic zones, thus increasing the intensity of your pleasure. You should coach your husband by letting him know how and where to stroke based on your pleasure sensation. Upon *sexperiencing* this pleasure, you and your husband should take note of what he is feeling and where he is stroking to aid in finding the G-spot area again.

JOY AND PAIN (J&P)

This aspect of lovemaking is exhorted only between the husband and wife who have a harmonious relationship. As with any form of sexual activity, you and your husband must mutually make love through seeking to out-serve and love the other. Joy and pain (J&P) should never be beatings, whippings, or hitting or with the intent to cause harm. You and your husband must always honor and respect each other. Christians are not to be abusive, degrading, or violent toward one another. Do not take what could be good (intensified sexual orgasmic pleasure) and make it evil (abusive).

The receiving of *mild* pain to an erogenous zone is a form of erotic play to intensify arousal and orgasm. Incorporating the pleasure of receiving mild pain has to be timed and administered appropriately and properly to achieve its desired effect. The key aspects of giving mild pain are listening and knowing the cues of the recipient.

Joy and Pain Techniques

Be sure you are highly aroused before he administers the mild pain, and you are continually aroused by the action. *Sexperiment* to identify which erogenous zones bring pleasure when pain is administered, such as biting or pinching of the nipples, biting of earlobes, pulling of the tongue, a light slap on the buttocks during intercourse to intensify arousal and orgasm, etc.

Always have a signal or a specific way of knowing when to stop. You both should understand that signal or specific code or action means to stop the pleasure. Make sure the code word or signal is not a word you use during erotic pleasure talk. If you use words such as *"no"* or *"stop,"* make sure the giver understands these terms mean *"no"* and *"stop"* and not that you are using them in a pleasurable connotation.

KISSING AND NECKING

Whatever happened to heavy petting and necking? Who said it had to stop when you said, *"I do!"*? Incorporate it again in your intimacy. Incorporate it every day of your marriage, from this day forward until death you do part. If you enjoy it, then *you* initiate hugging, kissing, necking, and heavy petting. You do not have to wait for your husband to initiate. Do away with the attitude of *"why don't he," "I wish he would," "he is supposed to,"* etc. That's a lie of the media, that the man is supposed to *always* initiate foreplay, kissing, hugging, caressing, petting, necking, and making love. Stop expecting your husband to do everything. If you have those expectations of your husband, do away with them right now! Have nothing to do with whoever or whatever (books, soap operas, TV, etc.) perpetrated that lie.

There is no sin for you to initiate and enjoy what gives you pleasure or gives pleasure to your husband. If you do not need to be hugged, kissed, etc., but your husband does, give him his pleasure. Consider his desires greater than your own (Philippians 2:3–4).

PHONE INTIMACY

Telephone intimacy gives a mental *sexcitement* for what is yet to come. Telephone intimacy with your husband can be a form of before-the-bedroom foreplay. Erotic telephone talk is a way to practice building up your confidence to be comfortable talking about sexual intimacy. You can learn how to be erotic and transparent via the telephone, then move to erotic pillow talk.

Get your husband's desire ignited by incorporating the following erotic talk tips:

- 🌱 Warm up by leaving erotic messages on his *private* voice mail.
- 🌱 Verbally give him a visual image of what he can enjoy when he arrives home.
- 🌱 Be *sexplicit* in what you want to do to him and what you want him to do to you. The *heat* of telephone sex is in the erotic, provocative details.
- 🌱 Be dramatic by using descriptive words and sound effects such as heavy breathing, panting, soft moans, etc.
- 🌱 Be prepared to give him what you have *sexcited* him for when the time comes. Tease to please!

U-DELIGHT

The urethra is a pleasure spot that must not be neglected in manual stimulation or oral lovemaking. *Sexperiment* to identify how to include this wonderful element in the pleasure sensation. For dynamic *sexhilarating sexplosion*: strum the clitoris and *U-Delight* with one hand, and with the other hand tease the anal area, while simultaneously making love orally to the perineum and every area of your *bed of pleasure*. If coordination is a concern for your husband or if you want other erogenous zones loved, consider love toys. Natural or water-soluble lubrication is a must for stimulating the *U-Delight* Spot. Refer to the sexual anatomy illustration in Chapter 8, *"Bed of Pleasure,"* for locating the *U-Delight* spot.

VOYEURISM

Voyeurism is defined here as the sexual arousal of observing or watching the act of lovemaking between you and your husband. Voyeurism can take lovemaking to an intense level of *sextreme* pleasure as you use the sense of sight God gave you to *sexamine* the act of lovemaking. Voyeurism between husband and wife can be *sex-hilarating* when you watch your husband make love to you orally, manually, as he undresses you, etc. You can select lovemaking positions that will allow you to watch him thrust his penis, finger, or tongue in and out of your vagina. Or, find positions that allow your husband to view your buttocks or his other favorite body parts and his penis thrusting in an out of your vagina, anus, or mouth.

Why are men so drawn to pornography? Men are aroused by sight. Your husband should never have to turn to pornography for the purpose of being *sexcited!* You should always be your husband's visual stimulation. You are fearfully and wonderfully made, so act like it! Allow your husband to be visually stimulated by you. Abide in the Word and be set free from any inhibitions or lies or falsehoods that hinder you from voyeuristically satisfying your husband.

IT'S IN THE POSITION

It is so amazing how God knitted your musculoskeletal system together to enable you to be flexible to maneuver into various love-making positions. What an awesome God! Indeed you are fearfully and wonderfully made and should enjoy lovemaking in every position possible. Certain positions intensify the pleasure and ignite the orgasmic fuse, specifically where the wife is in control of the angle and depth of penetration and the speed of thrusting. The wife can receive distinct *sexhilarating* sensations simply by shifting her body so the penis strokes and thrusts her vagina at different angles (hitting the G-Spot, the clitoris, etc.).

Sexperimenting with new positions requires patience as you take your time to learn what you can do to make the new position most effective. *Sexperimenting* with positions should be a playful time. Being too serious or having a perfectionistic mindset only takes away the *sexcitement* of trying something new. Do not get frustrated when trying a new position. Be patient as you *sexperiment*.

You must *sexperiment* to identify how to maneuver into some positions. Here are some tips for practicing:

- ♥ *Test.* Have a trial run, before actual use. Test getting into the position before lovemaking. Put new positions to the test when you have time to identify all the props and modifications needed to make the position feasible.
- ♥ *Not sexually aroused.* When you are at the brink of orgasm is not the time to try new positions. Do not try difficult positions when you are sexually aroused and your total focus is on making love.
- ♥ *Fully clothed.* Get in the position while you are dressed. Having clothes on will help you focus on practicing and not carrying out lovemaking.
- ♥ *Comfort.* It is important to be comfortable in every position. To elevate, prop, or rest your bodies, use pillows, blanket, rugs, walls, furniture, etc.
- ♥ *Laugh.* Have fun laughing and enjoying the trial run. Laughter enhances bonding.

❦ *Three-Strike Rule.* Try a position three times before it is discarded. You need not attempt all three trial runs in one *sexperiment* rendezvous (practice sessions). Give yourself some time between practice sessions to think about what you can do differently at the next practice session. Think of fun, exciting, creative ways to make the position work.

POSITIONS

Sexual positions are unlimited. Never allow yourself to get in the routine of making love in the same position all the time. Positions can be modified to accommodate for: conception and pregnancy; disabilities; physical or medical conditions; obesity; depth of penetration; sensation of the penis; and vaginal tightness. Factors to consider when choosing positions are: your comfort; your physical strength and endurance; maximum pleasure to each other; depth of penetration; thrusting ability; whether it is conducive to orgasm; voyeurism pleasure; and those that offer a potpourri of lovemaking methods while your husband is simultaneously using his hand, penis, love toy(s), and mouth to stimulate your clitoris, anus, and multiple other erogenous zones until you *sexplode* over and over again.

Positions can be modified to enhance and extend gratification by using pillows, rugs, blankets, and other items that give comfort and elevation; or props or supports for body reinforcement and thrusting such as floor, wall, stools, chairs, daybeds, tables, rocking chairs, any piece of furniture, or any supporting object.

This section has been adapted from the book *Sexplosion in Marriage: God's Gift of Intimacy in Lovemaking Positions* by Joe and Ramona Bailey. Reprinted with permission of the authors. For more about this book, refer to the "From the Author" page in this Workbook.

LOVE TOYS

A love toy is a device designed to prolong and intensify the love-making pleasure. Love toys should never be used for masturbation of self without your husband present. The marriage bed is for pleasure of the husband and wife, not for solo-pleasure independent of the husband (1 Corinthians 7:1–5). When you are abiding in the Word, you will have the proper perspective for the use of love toys. When you exclude your husband, you open the door to begin fantasizing about others, becoming dependent on the love toy, or replacing your husband with a love toy. Love toys are acceptable in the marriage bed to heighten sexual pleasure between the husband and wife. You and your husband must be in one accord regarding using love toys, the types, and when you will use them.

Love toys take *sexhilarating sexplosions to volcanic eruptions.* There are many occasions when love toys may be needed, such as fatigue, stimulation of multiple erogenous areas simultaneously, extend lovemaking, and for physical or health conditions.

Fatigue

When your husband's hands, fingers, tongue, or penis reaches fatigue and you are not finished *sexploding,* he can use a love toy until his body rejuvenates or until you have finished *sexploding.*

Multiple Erogenous Stimulation

Multiple love toys can bring you to *sexplosion* through stimulating your multiple erogenous zones. Stimulating multiple erogenous areas increases and intensifies multiple orgasmic pleasure. Love toys can aid your husband if he has difficulty coordinating his mouth, fingers, hands, and penis all at the same time. With love toys, he can give you simultaneous stimulation to multiple areas of your body. For example: With one hand he can stroke your G-Spot and with the other he can caress and massage your erogenous areas.

He uses a strap-on clitoral stimulator love toy for your clitoris, a vibrating anal love toy, vibrating nipple clamps for your breasts, his mouth for kissing, licking, and sucking your neck, lips, ears, and all your erogenous areas, and bondage toys to control your orgasmic, shattering body.

Extend Lovemaking

Love toys are good for before, during, and after lovemaking. After your husband has experienced an orgasm and you have not had or you want to continue having orgasms, he can continue to make love to you with love toys.

Physical or Health Conditions

Your husband can stimulate you with love toys if he is experiencing erection challenges. Love toys can be used when medical or health conditions hinder intercourse. Love toys can be used for anal stimulation and during your menstrual cycle. Love toys should be thoroughly washed after use in the anus before using in the vagina.

TIPS FOR USAGE

There are a wide variety of techniques and methods for enjoying love toys. You and your husband can *sexperiment* and enjoy the creativity of using love toys to take you to deeper intensified orgasmic *sexplosions*. Learn by *sexperimenting* with what is the right pressure and movement intensity for loving your delicate clitoris and anal areas with love toys. Pressure that is too strong or movement that is too intense may be a setback to the gratification being received. If there is not a speed or intensity control level, try placing a covering over the head of the vibrator/massager to lessen the vibrations. Suggested coverings are towels, socks, clothing, a pillow, etc.

Sexperimenting using love toys requires planning, patience, and practice. Do not become frustrated if initially the desired effect is not achieved. *Sexperimenting* turns bloopers into blessings. You must *sexpress* to your husband *when, where,* and *how* you would like him to use the love toy to your erogenous zones. Practice prior to making love. Plan to have everything ready and accessible before lovemaking.

In addition to those listed throughout the Workbook, some other considerations for use are:

- 💗 Stimulating the outer and inner vaginal lips.
- 💗 Stroking erogenous zones with long, slow, up and down movements.
- 💗 Snuggling it between the vaginal lips.
- 💗 Teasing by stopping and starting sensations.
- 💗 Arousing with long, steady and direct, yet gentle stimulation to the urethral or vaginal opening.
- 💗 Thrusting with slow and fast movements in and out of the vagina.
- 💗 Inserting a vibrating love toy in your vagina or anus, then turn it on and enjoy the vibrations as your husband makes love to your other erogenous zones.
- 💗 Operating multiple love toys simultaneously in every erogenous zone of your body.

PURCHASING TOYS

You can now add sensual intimacy products to the line of other in-home sale products, similar to the popular in-home sales of dishes, toys, or makeup. A few companies offer in-home sale parties and presentations of sensual intimacy products. In-home sensual product parties are designed for women. A popular Christian sensual intimacy provider is Solomon's Garden; contact them at www.solomonsgarden.com. These parties provide an opportunity to see, learn about, and purchase products. There are many advantages to in-home product parties versus the adult novelty sex stores or adult mail order catalog purchases. Some of the advantages of in-home parties over the adult novelty sex stores are:

- ❧ You may sample and observe some products.
- ❧ Your name, mailing address, or email address is not sold to other companies.
- ❧ Your purchase is not made in a public setting, but in private area.
- ❧ You are not exposed to homosexual or bestiality images.
- ❧ You can determine what items you want to have displayed in your home setting.
- ❧ Your personal questions can be addressed.
- ❧ The sales representative is a woman.

For the reasons listed above, in-home purchases of sensual products are preferred over mail-order catalogs or adult novelty sex stores. With the latter places, you may be exposed to nudity, homosexual activity, bestiality, and other sexual immoral acts.

SEXPLODE

This Workbook exhorts you to *sexperience* all that God, the Designer of *sexplosions,* intended. As you faithfully ASK—Abide in the Word, Serve to satisfy your husband, and apply the *"how to"* Knowledge—you should never return to your old lifestyle of sexual intimacy. You can remain in the *sexhilarating sexcitement* of *sexplosion in marriage.*

Exchanging old habits for new ones can be difficult if you fail to take the necessary steps to be victorious. As you *ASK*, it is imperative for you to establish and maintain Action Plans and acquire an Accountability Spiritual Support Partner (ASSP) to help you. You cannot have intimacy with your husband if you do not have spiritual intimacy with God (1 John 4:20).

Your commitment to abide in the Word is contingent upon you alone. If you choose to not sow obedience, you will not reap blessings. If you choose to be slothful in well doing, you will not have abundant blessings (Galatians 6:7–9; John 15:1–7). Choose this day whether you will abide in the Word or allow the cares of this world to choke out the seed of God's Word in these biblically based *sexplosion* principles (Matthew 13:18–23).

Appendices

A

Tips for Developing and Implementing an Action Plan

An **ACTION PLAN** is a road map to get you to where God would have you to be in your relationship with Him and with your spouse, and in other areas of your life. The following are some important considerations for developing and implementing an **ACTION PLAN**:

PRAYER

Seek God's wisdom, through praying and fasting, about how to develop and implement an Action Plan (Proverbs 16:3 TLB).

PURPOSE

Have an Objective. Be specific about what you want to accomplish. Have a goal to achieve. If practical, aim to achieve the goal by a designated time.

Be Sincere. An Action Plan should not be *just* another *"project to do."* You should have a fervent desire to be a doer of God's Word and not just to know what the Word says.

Be Committed. Be committed to make a permanent transformation in your life to abide in the Word as you achieve your objective.

Establish a Plan. Ensure you have covered all possible obstacles that would be a hindrance or distraction.

PROVISIONS

Where possible, develop the Action Plan to be totally contingent on you alone and on no one else.

If the Action Plan is contingent upon others, make sure you are responsible for accomplishing your tasks. Focus on doing what you need to do, not on what others are not doing.

PLAN

Be in Harmony. If the Plan is contingent upon your spouse, both of you must be in harmony with each other's goals, desires, and plans.

Be Effective. For the plan to be effective, you must identify the strengths and weaknesses of the Plan. Adapt the weaknesses so they will become strengths.

Grow Spiritually. Incorporate biblical principles that will help you grow spiritually.

Be Thorough. The Plan should:

- ❦ Include biblical principles for your objective.
- ❦ Detail exactly how you will be obedient to God.
- ❦ Identify the specific sin you need to acknowledge, confess, repent of, seek forgiveness for, or forgive others of.
- ❦ Identify and address your specific challenge (problem). Get to the root of the matter, not just surface issues.
- ❦ Incorporate practical guidelines for putting off old practices and putting on better practices.
- ❦ Outline steps for how you will resist the devil when he seeks to hinder you from carrying out your Plan.
- ❦ Renew your mind and the words you speak to be in agreement with God's Word.
- ❦ List consequences if you become slothful or fail to make lifestyle changes.
- ❦ Choose the best techniques, steps, and methods for accomplishing the objective of your Action Plan.

PERIOD OF TIME

Set a Timetable. Have a deadline or timetable for when you will have your objective achieved.

Evaluate. Periodically evaluate your progress in achieving your objective. Consider evaluating on a monthly, bimonthly, or quarterly timetable.

Make Revisions. As you evaluate your progress, make revisions for enhancements as needed. Do not become stagnant; always seek to grow and make improvements.

PARTNERS

Seek Godly Counsel. Identify a godly ASSP, who is totally committed to **ABIDING** in the Word, to give you wise godly counsel regarding your Action Plan.

ASSP. Obtain an Accountability/Spiritual Support Partner (ASSP). Refer to ASSP Guidelines, Appendix B.

Abide in the Word

*"We should make plans—counting
on God to direct us."*
(Proverbs 16:9 TLB)

*"Commit your work to the Lord,
then it will succeed."*
(Proverbs 16:3 TLB)

B

Accountability/ Spiritual Support Partner (ASSP) Guidelines

WHAT?

Accountability/Spiritual Support Partner (ASSP).

WHY?

- ❦ To hold you accountable to **ABIDE** in the Word (John 15:4–7).
- ❦ To hold you accountable to fulfill your Action Plan (refer to *"Tips for Developing and Implementing An Action Plan,"* Appendix A).
- ❦ To pray with and for you as you carry out your Action Plan. To correct, rebuke, and encourage you with great patience and careful instruction (2 Timothy 4:2).
- ❦ To bring you back when you wander away (James 5:19–20).
- ❦ To cheer you up when you feel that all hope is gone (Proverbs 12:25).

WHEN?

Pray for God to identify an ASSP for you. Do not be slothful in obtaining an ASSP. Take immediate action to obtain an ASSP. Be determined to have an ASSP within one week.

WHO?

Only a godly married female should serve as an ASSP for another female (never a male serving a female). The ASSP:

- ❦ Is committed to being obedient to God's Word.

- Is not just a hearer of the Word, but a doer.
- Is faithful to the facts of God's Word and does not fluctuate on circumstances because of her emotions or feelings.
- Will take the time to execute the role of an ASSP, as listed herein.
- Will be sincere, open, honest, transparent, and objective.
- Is honest, bold, and not slothful in encouraging, rebuking, and praying with you.
- Will be committed to hold you accountable.
- Values living by the Word of God more than maintaining your friendship or hurting your feelings because you must be corrected or admonished.

Who to Avoid

End the accountability relationship immediately and find someone else if:

- Your ASSP becomes slothful or ineffective in holding you accountable.
- After adjusting your accountability contact schedule, she is frequently unavailable, or she never returns your calls.
- She is living in an unrepentant lifestyle of sin or makes excuses for a sinful life.
- She is already involved in too many activities, functions, etc. that take away quality time from her family.
- Your spouse disapproves of the ASSP relationship.
- Your ASSP's spouse flirts with you or acts inappropriately with you.
- She fails to follow through in areas you have repeatedly asked her to hold you accountable to do.

HOW?

- ❦ Make contact one day a week at a designated time.
- ❦ Conversation should pertain only to accountability matters.
- ❦ Inform the ASSP what you want to be held accountable to do. Refer to your Action Plan(s) you should have developed.
- ❦ Inform the ASSP what will be the most effective way to rebuke and admonish you if you become slothful or disobedient in fulfilling your Action Plan.
- ❦ Set deadlines for when your assignments, projects, goals will be completed.
- ❦ When you contact one another do not degrade spouses, or have pity party or *"let's whine about our spouse"* conversations.

 Abide in the Word

"Two can accomplish more than twice as much as one, for the results can be much better. If one falls, the other pulls him up; but if a man falls when he is alone, he's in trouble."
(Ecclesiastes 4:9–10 TLB)

C

Reference Notes and Spiritual Growth Resources

Materials marked with this symbol: are reference sources for additional information on subject or topics addressed in the Workbook. All other materials can be used to aid in your spiritual growth.

CHAPTER 1

Arthur, Kay. *How to Study Your Bible, Precept Upon Precept.* Harvest House Publishers, 1994.

Bible Resources to Help You Grow. Radio Bible Class Ministries Discovery Series. A brochure listing over 140 spiritual growth booklets. To obtain a brochure listing all of the available topics, contact www.rbc.net or www.discoveryseries.org.

Deison, Peter V. *Time With God- Quality Intimate Time With God.* Radio Bible Class Ministries Discovery Series. Grand Rapids Michigan: Discovery House Publishers, 1992. www.rbc.net.

Evans, Tony. *Fasting: Keys to Spiritual Victory.* Six Cassette Tape Album, 1999. www.tonyevans.org.

Flaten, Dick. *The Marvelous Exchange, Discovering the Power of Spiritual Union with Christ: An Exposition on Romans 6:1–14.* Exchanged Life Ministries Texas, 1999. www.exchangedlife.org.

 Merriam-Webster Online Collegiate® Dictionary, © 2002.

Our Daily Bread—For Personal and Family Devotions. Radio Bible Class Ministries. To receive this monthly day to day devotional, contact www.rbc.net.

The Strong's Exhaustive Concordance of the Bible. Virginia: Macdonald Publishing Company.

Wilkinson, Bruce. *Secrets of the Vine.* Sisters, Oregon: Multnomah Publishers, Inc., 2001.

CHAPTER 2

Allender, Dan B. *When Trust Is Lost—Healing for Victims of Sexual Abuse.* Radio Bible Class Ministries Discovery Series. Grand Rapids, Michigan: Discovery House Publishers, 1992. www.rbc.net

 American College of Physicians Complete Home Medical Guide. DK Publishing, Inc., 1999. www.dk.com.

Hunt, June. *Childhood Sexual Abuse: The Secret Storm. Biblical Counseling Keys.* Hope for the Heart, 2001. 1–800–488–HOPE; www.hopefortheheart.org.

Hunt, June. *Rape Recovery: Rescued and Restored. Biblical Counseling Keys.* Hope for the Heart, 1999. 1–800–488–HOPE; www.hopefortheheart.org.

Hunt, June. *Sexual Addiction: How to Make the Break. Biblical Counseling Keys.* Hope for the Heart, 2001. 1–800–488–HOPE; www.hopefortheheart.org

Hunt, June. *Sexual Temptation: Looking for Love in All the Wrong Places. Biblical Counseling Keys.* Hope for the Heart, 2000. 1–800–488–HOPE; www.hopefortheheart.org.

Jackson, Tim. *When A Spouse Is Unfaithful.* Radio Bible Class Ministries Discovery Series. Grand Rapids, Michigan: Discovery House Publishers, 1999. www.rbc.net.

McIlhaney, Joe S., Jr., M.D. *1001 Health-Care Questions Women Ask.* Baker Books, 1998.

 Merck Manual of Medical Information: Home Edition. Section 7, Mental Health Disorders; Chapter 87, Sexuality and Psychosexual Disorders; Chapter 88, Disorders of Sexual Function. Merck Research Laboratories, 1997.

 Merriam-Webster Online Collegiate® Dictionary, © 2002.

 Murphy, Ed, M.D. *The Handbook of Spiritual Warfare.* Cambridge, Ontario: Thomas Nelson Publishers, Inc., 1992.

CHAPTER 3

Allender, Dan B. *When Trust Is Lost—Healing for Victims of Sexual Abuse.* Radio Bible Class Ministries Discovery Series. Grand Rapids, Michigan: Discovery House Publishers, 1992. www.rbc.net.

Anderson, Neil T. *Living Free in Christ.* Ventura, California: Regal Books, 1993.

Deison, Peter V. *Time With God—Quality Intimate Time With God.* Radio Bible Class Ministries Discovery Series. Grand Rapids, Michigan: Discovery House Publishers, 1992. www.rbc.net.

Focus on the Family Ministry online resources for pornography and sexual addiction. www.family.org; 1–800–A–FAMILY (232–6459).

Hunt, June. *Childhood Sexual Abuse: The Secret Storm. Biblical Counseling Keys.* Hope for the Heart, 2001. 1–800–488–HOPE; www.hopefortheheart.org

Hunt, June. *Rape Recovery: Rescued and Restored.* *Biblical Counseling Keys.* Hope for the Heart, 1999. 1–800–488–HOPE; www.hopefortheheart.org.

Hunt, June. *Sexual Addiction: How to Make the Break.* *Biblical Counseling Keys.* Hope for the Heart, 2001. 1–800–488–HOPE; www.hopefortheheart.org.

Hunt, June. *Sexual Temptation: Looking for Love in All the Wrong Places.* *Biblical Counseling Keys.* Hope for the Heart, 2000. 1–800–488–HOPE; www.hopefortheheart.org.

Hunt, June. *Stress: Beating Burnout Before It Beats You.* *Biblical Counseling Keys.* Hope for the Heart, 2001. 1–800–488–HOPE; www.hopefortheheart.org.

 Masters, William H., M.D, and Virginia E. Johnson. *Human Sexual Response.* Chapter 8, "Uterine Response During Menstruation." Boston: Little, Brown and Company, 1966.

McGee, Robert S. *The Search for Significance Book and Workbook.* Houston, Texas: Rapha Publishing, 1990.

Sherrer, Quin, and Ruthanne Garlock. *A Woman's Guide to Spiritual Warfare.* Ann Arbor, Michigan: Servant Publications, Vine Books, 1991.

CHAPTER 4

Jackson, Tim. *When the Flame Flickers—Rekindling Intimacy In Your Marriage.* Radio Bible Class Ministries Discovery Series. Grand Rapids, Michigan: Discovery House Publishers, 2001. www.rbc.net.

Merck Manual of Medical Information: Home Edition. Section 7, Mental Health Disorders; Chapter 87, Sexuality and Psychosexual Disorders; Chapter 88, Disorders of Sexual Function. Merck Research Laboratories, 1997.

Murphey, Cecil B. *The Encyclopedia of Christian Marriage.* Chapter 3, Husband and Wife. Grand Rapids, Michigan: Fleming H. Revell, a division of Baker Book House Company, 1984.

CHAPTER 5

Whipple, Beverly, PhD., RN, FAAN, Professor Emerita, Rutgers University; President-Elect, Society for the Scientific Study of Sexuality; Vice-President, World Association for Sexology (2001–2005). For a listing of her *"Recent Publications Concerning Sexuality,"* contact: bwhipple@recom-net.net.

CHAPTER 7

Bailey, Joe and Ramona. *Sexplosion in Marriage: God's Gift of Intimacy in Lovemaking Positions.* "It's in the Position," Positional Illustration P–01. Bailey, Joe and Ramona, 2003. To obtain this book, contact: www.Abideintheword.org.

CHAPTER 8

Bantam Medical Dictionary. Third Revised Edition. Market House Books Ltd., 1981, 1990, 1994, 2000.

Burton, Michael, O.D., First Eye Care, Dallas, Texas, June 2002

Merck Manual of Medical Information Home Edition. Section 1, Fundamentals, Chapter 1, Anatomy; Section 6, Chapter 59, Biology of the Nervous System; Section 13, Hormonal Disorders, Chapter 143, Endocrine System and Hormones. Merck Research Laboratories, 1997.

Weight Management Resource: The Weigh Down Workshop. 1–800–340–2141; www.wdworkshop.com; P.O. Box 689099, Franklin, TN 37068.

CHAPTER 9

Bailey, Joe and Ramona. *Sexplosion in Marriage: God's Gift of Intimacy in Lovemaking Positions.* "It's in the Position," Positional Illustrations P–01 through P–07. Joe and Ramona Bailey, 2003. To obtain this book, contact: www.Abideintheword.org.

Dr. Ruth's Encyclopedia of Sex. The Jerusalem Publishing House Ltd. Continuum International Publishing Group, 1994.

Greggs, Sharon E., M.D., Fellow American College of Gynecology (FACOG), Dallas, Texas, June 2002.

Jackson, Tim, and Mart De Haan. *Designed for Desire—God's Design for Sexuality.* Radio Bible Class Ministries Discovery Series. Grand Rapids, Michigan: Discovery House Publishers, 1993. www.rbc.net.

McCurley, LeeRoy M.D., Board Certified Family Practitioner, Dallas, Texas, May 2002.

Murphey, Cecil B. *The Encyclopedia of Christian Marriage.* Chapter 4, Sex and Reproduction. Grand Rapids, Michigan: Fleming H. Revell, a division of Baker Book House Company, 1984. [

Whipple, Beverly, PhD., RN, FAAN, Professor Emerita, Rutgers University; President-Elect, Society for the Scientific Study of Sexuality; Vice-President, World Association for Sexology (2001–2005). For a listing of her *"Recent Publications Concerning Sexuality,"* contact: bwhipple@recom-net.net.

References to any specific medical provider, researcher, agency, commercial product or process, or service by trade name, trademark, service mark, brand, manufacturer, or otherwise does not constitute or imply endorsement or favoring by the author or others affiliated with writing and publication of this Workbook. Commercial products referenced are not known Christian-based businesses or affiliates, unless noted.

Subject Index

Scripture Index

OLD TESTAMENT

NEW TESTAMENT

From the Author

*T*hank you for investing in your marriage by applying these biblical *sexplosion* principles. It is my prayer that you will *sexperience* a lifetime of *sexplosions* in your marriage as you abide in the Word. You may send your *sexplosion* testimonials or help you received from this Workbook to my address listed below. Contact me at Abide in the Word for more marriage resource material or for speaking at conferences or if you would like to attend a conference.

Request your local bookstore to offer *Sexplosion: A Biblically Based Sexual Intimacy Workbook for Wives*, ISBN: 1-591605-40-7 available to their customers. Forthcoming materials in the Sexplosion In Marriage Series ™ are:

❣ *SEXPLOSION IN MARRIAGE: God's Gift of Intimacy In Lovemaking Positions* by Joe and Ramona Bailey.

❣ *SEXPLOSION FOR HUSBANDS* series by Joe E. Bailey.

To obtain additional copies of this book and other resources, contact:

RAMONA BAILEY
Abide In The Word
P.O. Box 271237
Dallas, Texas 75227–1237 USA
www.Abideintheword.org.

Enjoy God's blessing of *Sexplosion in marriage!*

Sincerely Abiding in the Word (John 15:4–7),
Ramona Nelson Bailey
2003

ORDER FORM
Bless other wives! Purchase a copy for them today.

ABIDE IN THE WORD
Sexplosion In Marriage Series ™
P.O. Box 271237 • Dallas, TX 75227-1237

Please print legibly.
Quantity Books Ordered: _____ @ $ 16.99 each
Total: $ _____

Shipping & Handling Cost:
   ($2.90 per book) $_____

Total Order Cost: $_____

PAYMENT INFORMATION—Do Not Send Cash.
   Make checks payable to Ramona Bailey. If Submitting Check, Allow Three (3) Week Deliver Time for Order.

Charge: ❑ VISA   ❑ MasterCard
Card Number: _____
Date Card Expires: _____
Name on Card: _____
Signature: _____

SHIPPING INFORMATION
Ship Material To (Give Your Street Address, Not P.O. Box for Shipping)

Contact Name: _____
Organization: _____
Mailing Address: _____
City, State, Zip Code: _____
Daytime Telephone Number: _____

You may also make orders through the publisher Xulon Press.
Contact Xulon Press Order Department toll-free at
1-866-909-BOOK (2665).

CPSIA information can be obtained at www.ICGtesting.com
Printed in the USA
LVOW062209080412

276715LV00002B/128/A